A PRACTICAL
ORGANIC
CHEMISTRY

BLACKIE & SON LIMITED
5 FITZHARDINGE STREET
PORTMAN SQUARE
LONDON · W.1
BISHOPBRIGGS, GLASGOW

**BLACKIE & SON
(INDIA) LIMITED**
103-5 FORT STREET
BOMBAY

A
PRACTICAL
ORGANIC
CHEMISTRY

D. C. FIRTH B.Sc

Head of the Scientific Department
The Bristol Grammar School

1809
Lucem Libris
Disseminamus

BLACKIE & SON LIMITED

LONDON

GLASGOW

FIRST PUBLISHED 1966

PRINTED IN GREAT BRITAIN BY BLACKIE & SON LIMITED · GLASGOW

PREFACE

Organic compounds fall very naturally into groups or homologous series. Each series is characterized by common methods of preparation and similar chemical properties. Similarity within the group is widely used in studying the subject. It is standard practice to study one member of each series in some detail, and to derive the chemistry of other members in the knowledge that they are of the same group. Inorganic chemistry may be treated in the same way—we can divide 'oxides' into types: acidic, basic, amphoteric, etc., so that within each type the methods of preparation and the properties are similar.

It is very useful to consider organic chemistry from another point of view. Given a great deal of information about the reactions, we can divide *these* into classes. In this way, reductions, oxidations, dehydrations, etc., become the subjects of study. Under each type of reaction, the reagents which bring it about, and its mechanism, become the subjects of study. In this book, matter is arranged to show the types of chemical reaction common in organic chemistry; reagents in common use are described, and their application illustrated.

Where appropriate, ionic equations are used to represent chemical reactions. There is little merit in regarding organic chemistry as 'the study of covalent bonds', and any theme which integrates the branches of the subject is worthy of serious consideration.

In discussing oxidation/reduction reactions, the conventions of electron transfer are used. Why should we use electron-transfer ideas in interpreting inorganic reactions, but use the [H] and [O] system when we consider carbon compounds?

Mechanism studies are often complicated, demanding equipment outside the facilities of a school or college laboratory. Such methods as the detection of intermediates using 'labelled' atoms, are techniques to be learned at post-graduate level. On the other hand, it is possible to do a few rate experiments, appreciating that they often give insight into mechanisms.

A short discussion of how reactions work is included at the beginning of each chapter.

One problem when writing about preparative chemistry is that of selecting experiments. Ideally, reactants should be common chemicals, and the products formed be easy to isolate. Most of the experiments described do satisfy these conditions. Another problem is that of scale and the type of glassware to be used. Semi-micro interchangeable glassware is used throughout, and quantities of reactants are 10–15g. Work is faster and safer this way, and it is probably cheaper.

Preparative experiments are often judged in terms of the light they shed on general principles. Certain dangers attend this point of view, and additional values are necessary. A preparation must be judged by considering the cost of the reactants, the time taken, and the yields obtained. It is of the greatest importance to measure the last two and to record them. The quality of the product must be considered too, and some time must be devoted to judging this. Wherever possible, melting points or boiling points should be recorded.

I make no apology for the regular statement of 'cautions'. It is tempting to write hazards into a single chapter, and to hope that the student will read it and remember it. Like a title page, this presentation is often overlooked, and references to it may be ignored. It does seem best to preface each experiment with the necessary warnings.

D. C. FIRTH

THE BRISTOL GRAMMAR SCHOOL
January, 1966

CONTENTS

Semimicro Apparatus

1

Practical chemistry may be conducted on the macro, semimicro, or micro scale. The terms refer to the quantities being used in the work. For a preparation, the scale used will depend on how much product is required. 50 g would be called a large-scale or 'macro' preparation, 5 g a semimicro and 0·5 g a micro preparation. Similarly, the analysis of a 5 g sample would be termed 'macro analysis', whilst work on 0·05 g would count as 'micro analysis'. Micro work demands special equipment and a great deal of skill; general laboratories are quite unsuitable for it.

Ground-glass joints

Cork and rubber bungs are difficult to use and very often they are inefficient. Work is speeded up if ground-glass joints are used. At the same time it is possible to misuse this kind of apparatus, and mistakes are very expensive. The following points should be studied carefully.

1. Before use, make sure that ground-glass joints are free from grit. Make it a habit to wipe them over before use.

2. Separate the joint as soon as possible after use. If pieces stay in contact for a long time, they may bind together. If seizure does occur, release by applying a gentle heat to the socket using a micro burner. Fan the flame over the socket.

Heating

3. Never heat a flask locally; a flame should act over all the glass in contact with liquid. To reduce the heat, move the burner away. Do not reduce the flame so that it acts locally.

4. Use a water-bath when heating volatile inflammable liquids (a small beaker serves quite well for this purpose). An ordinary Bunsen

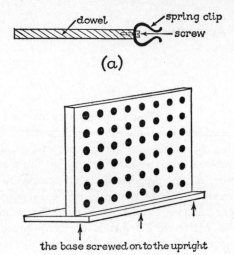

(a)

(b)

the base screwed on to the upright

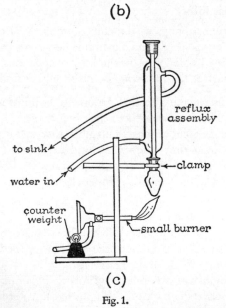

(c)

Fig. 1.

burner is quite unsuitable for direct heating. Use the Bunsen with the barrel removed, or better still, use a micro burner.

Clamping

5. Ground-glass joints give an assembly rigidity, and clamping must not be excessive. Ordinary stands and clamps are too large, and it is useful to construct supports in wood.

A piece of dowel (diameter $\frac{3}{8}$ in and length 6 in) with a spring clip screwed on one end will serve as a clamp (fig. 1*a*).

A stand may be made from $\frac{3}{4}$ in plywood. A piece about 14 in × 14 in is drilled with a regular pattern of holes, of such a size that the dowel rod may be inserted. Another piece is screwed on to act as the base (fig. 1*b*).

Figure 1*c* is an assembly using this method of support.

2

Notes

Many organic compounds have definite melting points, the values of which serve to identify the substances. A melting point alone is not sufficient evidence for an identification, because it sometimes happens that two or more solids melt at the same temperature. Some materials do not have a melting point— sugar, for example, will begin to decompose when it is heated. Similarly, many materials sublime on heating. Melting points are often used as a criterion of purity. As a rule, an impurity depresses the melting point of a substance, and the extent of the depression gives some indication of how much impurity is present. The routine of purifying a solid is marked by measuring its melting point at intervals, and the progress made may be followed in this way.

The value of the method for identifying substances is increased if *mixed melting points* are measured. Suppose an unidentified substance X is found to have the same melting point ($T_X°C$) as two other substances A and B, and other evidence suggests that X is in fact one or the other. Mixtures AX and BX may be prepared and their melting points determined ($T_{AX}°C$ and $T_{BX}°C$ respectively).

If $T_{AX}°C = T_X°C$, then X is compound A.

If $T_{BX}°C = T_X°C$, then X is compound B.

If, for example, an unidentified white crystalline solid has a melting point of 122°C, and it shows reactions typical of an organic acid, then it is almost certainly benzoic acid ($C_6H_5 . COOH$, m.p. 122°C). This may be confirmed by mixing the white solid with benzoic acid and then measuring the melting point of the mixture. A value of 122°C is very strong confirmation.

Method

A melting-point apparatus is shown in fig. 2, and this must be assembled very carefully because it is a permanent piece of equipment. The capillary tubes are made by softening wide-bore glass tubing in a batswing flame, and drawing it out. The capillary tube is then broken into pieces about two inches long. One end of each tube is sealed off by rotating it in a flame for a few seconds. It is useful to make a stock of tubes and keep them in a corked test-tube.

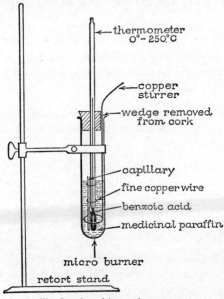

thermometer
0°– 250.°C

copper
stirrer

wedge removed
from cork

capillary

fine copper wire

benzoic acid

medicinal paraffin

micro burner

retort stand

Fig. 2.—A melting-point apparatus

Experiment 1. To measure the melting point of benzoic acid

Grind a little benzoic acid to a fine powder using a clean dry pestle and mortar. Introduce a little of the powder into the neck of a capillary, and shake the tube so that the solid falls to the closed end. This is difficult if the solid is damp or if the grinding has not been thorough. Attach the capillary to the thermometer using fine copper wire, and gently heat some medicinal paraffin using a micro burner. The liquid must be stirred all the time. Note the temperature at which the solid melts. Repeat the experiment to obtain a second value.

Add a little salicylic acid to the rest of the benzoic acid in the mortar, grind the mixture, and then determine its melting point.

THE DETERMINATION OF BOILING POINTS

Notes

The boiling point of a liquid might help in its identification, or it might be measured to assess the purity of the liquid. Boiling point is influenced by atmospheric pressure, and in very accurate determinations allowance is made for this.

If the pressure is p mmHg, and the measured boiling point is $t°C$, then ΔT, the correction to be added to give the boiling point at 760 mmHg, may be calculated from the equation

$$\Delta T = 0 \cdot 000\,12(273 + t)(760 - p)$$

Usually the correction is ignored, as thermometers used for the determination of t are very often calibrated in one-degree units only. If the pressure is very low (740 mmHg) and the liquid has a high boiling point (200°C), the correction would be of the order of one degree.

One serious limitation of the technique is that many liquids begin to decompose at temperatures below their boiling points. A darkening of the liquid often gives an indication of this.

The graphs shown in fig. 3 show how boiling-point determinations may be used to judge the purity of a liquid. A mixture boils over a range of temperatures, whereas a pure substance has a very limited range.

Some liquids may be superheated, and 'bumping' occurs when boiling starts. A few pieces of porous pot should be added to the liquid under study to prevent this from happening. Boiling occurs when the vapour pressure of a liquid reaches atmospheric pressure, and when this pressure is generated in spaces beneath the surface of the liquid. Without these spaces the temperature can rise above the normal boiling point and the liquid is said to be superheated. Porous pot provides the free spaces, and prevents the very violent onset of boiling.

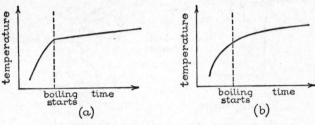

Fig. 3.—Boiling-point ranges for pure and impure liquids

If a boiling point is to be measured using a large volume of liquid, then the vapour must be condensed. A Liebig condenser is used if the boiling point is less than 150°C; above this an air condenser is efficient. A drained Liebig condenser is very inefficient; it might even crack; and it must never be used for this purpose.

Experiment 2. To measure the boiling point of chloroform

A. *Using a large quantity of liquid*

CAUTION: Do not leave stock alcohol on the bench.

Use the apparatus shown in fig. 4 to measure the boiling point. Place 15 ml of chloroform in the pear-shaped flask and heat it using a water-bath. When boiling starts, record the temperature every minute.

Repeat the experiment but use a mixture of 10 ml industrial spirit and 5 ml of water in the flask. Heat the flask directly with a small flame. Note the temperature every minute.

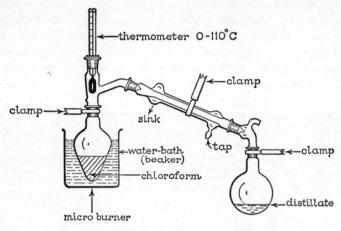

Fig. 4.—The measurement of boiling points (large scale)
Use dry apparatus

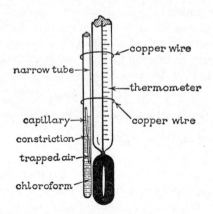

Fig. 5.—The boiling point of small quantities
This shows how the melting-point apparatus is modified to determine
boiling points

B. *Using a small quantity of liquid*

A melting-point apparatus (fig. 2) may be modified for this purpose. Cut a piece of narrow glass tubing about 3 in long and seal one end in a Bunsen flame. Allow the tube to cool. Transfer chloroform into the tube using a dropper, until there is a depth of about 1 in. Make a constriction in a melting-point tube about $\frac{1}{2}$ in from one end, by heating it locally at this point. Put the capillary (open end first) into the chloroform and then fasten the tube to the thermometer as shown in fig. 5. Set the assembly in the medicinal paraffin and warm it gently. Note the evolution of bubbles from the capillary and record the temperature at which a rapid stream occurs. This is the boiling point. (The pressure of the vapour is one atmosphere.) Compare the value with that from the last experiment.

The Purification of Organic Compounds by
Physical Methods

3

A. RECRYSTALLIZATION

Solids are usually purified by recrystallizing them from a suitable solvent, and the choice of this demands some thought. We can imagine the ideal solvent:

1. It should be inexpensive.
2. It must be safe, non-poisonous, non-inflammable.
3. The solubility of the substance to be purified must be great at high temperature and low when the solvent is cold.
4. It must be inert—not reacting with the solute.

Sometimes these conditions are best satisfied by mixed solvents, and many of these are in common use.

The correct choice of solvent does not of itself lead to success in this work. Common mistakes include:

1. The use of too much solvent.
2. Filtrations using cold funnels and flasks.
3. The use of a solvent which allows the deposition of solute at temperatures above its melting point. A 'cake' results, and this is difficult to wash.

Careless recrystallizations will result in low yields, impure products, the wasting of time, and sometimes laboratory fires.

Sometimes a recrystallization is made more effective by boiling the solution with charcoal before allowing it to cool. The charcoal will often adsorb impurities, and these remain with the charcoal when the mixture is filtered.

Experiment 3. To purify benzoic acid—a recrystallization from water

Mix a little benzoic acid with a few drops of litmus, and then purify the acid in the following way. First, place a Büchner flask and funnel in an oven set at 100°C so that they are ready for use later. Heat 100 ml of water in a beaker on a tripod and gauze. When the water is hot (90°C) add the impure acid a little at a time,

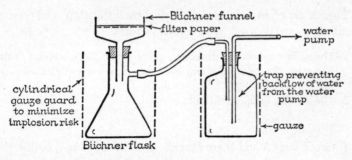

Fig. 6.—The apparatus for filtration

stirring constantly, and continue the addition until no more solid dissolves. Now boil the solution and add a spatula of charcoal. Boil the solution for two minutes. Set up the hot Büchner as shown in fig. 6 and, using a guard, apply suction and filter the mixture quickly. Transfer the solution to a dish and allow it to cool. Filter off the crystals, wash them with cold water, and draw air through them to remove most of the water. Dry the benzoic acid in a desiccator. Benzoic acid melts at 122°C.

Experiment 4. To purify acetamide—a recrystallization from an inflammable solvent

Work in a fume cupboard. Mix 15 ml of ethyl acetate and 50 ml of benzene in a beaker. Place the mixture in a water-bath and heat this until the solvent is almost boiling. Add acetamide and stir until no more will dissolve. Suction filter the solution using a hot Büchner, transfer the hot solution to a dish, and allow it to cool. Filter off the crystals and dry them in an oven at 50°C. Acetamide melts at 82°C.

B. DISTILLATION

Liquids are often isolated and purified by distillation. The type of distillation used depends upon several factors.

1. The difference between the boiling point of the liquid and that of the impurity. The greater this difference the easier it is to obtain a separation.
2. The stability of the liquid to be isolated.

If two liquids A and B are miscible and the mixture is boiled, the vapour produced will contain both A and B but will be richer in the more volatile liquid. The distillate first collected will be richer in the more volatile liquid, but will still contain some of the other. If this distillate is redistilled, then the vapour condensed will be still richer in the more volatile substance. This process may be repeated until a liquid is obtained which is pure enough for use. The greater the difference in boiling points, the fewer the operations required. Figure 8a illustrates the process of *fractional distillation*.

The labour involved in fractional distillation is reduced by using a fractionating column (fig. 7). At any point in such a column, we can regard a distillate condensed at some higher point, being redistilled by hot vapour rising from below.

Separation of A and B becomes difficult if the mixture provides a vapour whose composition is that of the liquid. Such a system is called a *constant boiling mixture*. Figure 8b illustrates this.

If a liquid decomposes at or below its normal boiling point then it may be purified by *vacuum distillation*. Here the pressure above the liquid is reduced so that it will boil at a lower temperature.

In fig. 8*a* the line XQY represents the variation of boiling point with composition of mixture AB. X is the boiling point of A and Y that of pure B. The line XPY represents the composition of the vapour produced when AB is boiled, so that a liquid of composition C_5, boils at $t_5°$, and produces a vapour whose composition is C_4.

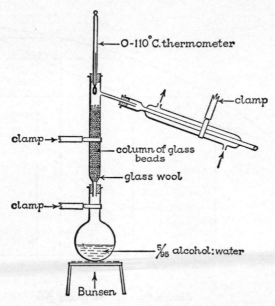

Fig. 7.—Fractional distillation

If we must obtain pure A from a mixture of composition C_1, then on its first distillation, it will boil at $t_1°$. The vapour obtained will have a composition C_2, and if this is condensed we will have a liquid of composition C_2. If this is redistilled it will boil at $t_2°$, and the vapour produced will have composition C_3. This may be condensed and further distilled until the sample of A is satisfactory.

In fig. 8*b* the line XPZSY represents the boiling point of various mixtures of A and B. Again X and Y represent the boiling points of the pure compounds A and B. The line XQZRY represents the composition of the vapour when any mixture is boiled. It will be seen that a mixture of composition C_2, boils at a temperature t_2, and

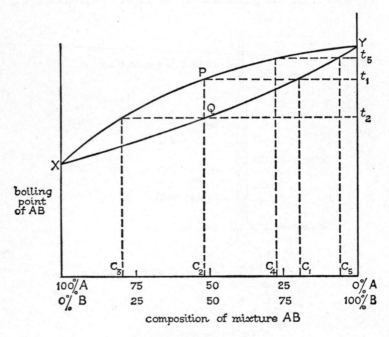

Fig. 8a.—Fractional distillation

that at this temperature the vapour has the same composition as the liquid. Such a mixture would distil unchanged. Because of this, the fractional distillation of mixture C_1 cannot produce pure B. It would boil at $t_1°$ and the residual liquid would become progressively richer in B. When the remaining liquid reached the composition C_2, it would distil unchanged.

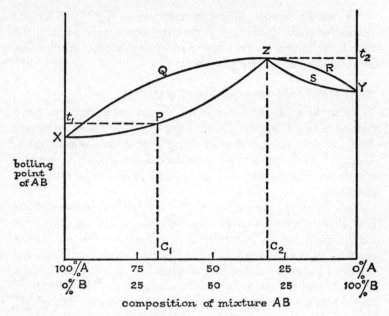

Fig. 8b.—Constant boiling mixture

Experiment 5. To study the efficiency of separating ethanol/water

CAUTION: Remove the stock alcohol from the bench after preparing the mixtures.

Prepare a mixture of 4 ml industrial spirit and 10 ml water. Stir the mixture and transfer a few drops into a crucible. Try to ignite the liquid. Pour the remaining liquid into the distillation apparatus (fig. 4), after making sure that the condenser is clean and dry. Heat the mixture and collect the first few drops of distillate. Try to ignite them.

Repeat the experiment but use a portion of a mixture containing 5 ml of industrial spirit and 95 ml of water. Try to ignite the first few drops of distillate.

Set up the fractional-distillation apparatus (fig. 7). Place the remainder of the $\frac{5}{95}$ mixture in the flask, connect the column, and then heat the mixture on a tripod and gauze. Collect the first few drops of distillate and try to ignite it.

Experiment 6. The vacuum distillation of glycerol

Set up the apparatus shown in fig. 9a, use an air condenser and a thermometer reading to 300°C. Pour 10 ml of glycerol into the flask and distil the liquid using direct heat from a micro burner. Usually the glycerol will begin to decompose at its boiling point, and the liquid in the flask will darken. The distillate might be yellow in colour.

Now set up the apparatus (fig. 9b) arranged for vacuum distillation. Pour 10 ml of glycerol into the three-necked flask. One of the necks should contain a thermometer set in the still head, another contains a piece of glass tubing drawn out to a fine capillary, and the third is stoppered. The rate at which air enters the flask under reduced pressure is controlled using a screw clip, Y. The receiver is a round-bottomed flask, and the apparatus is evacuated through the side-arm, X. The apparatus is connected to the water-pump via a trap, *and the apparatus is screened by supporting a piece of transparent polythene sheet in front of it.*

Reduce the pressure in the apparatus SLOWLY, and regulate Y so that a small flow of air enters the flask. Heat the flask using a low flame. Note the temperature at which the glycerol distils, and assess the extent of decomposition by noting any darkening of the liquid. Compare these observations with those obtained in the last experiment.

Steam distillation

An insoluble substance A, which has an appreciable vapour pressure at the boiling point of water, may be separated from substances of negligible vapour pressure by using the technique of steam distillation. The isolations of essential oils from fruits, and perfumes from flower petals, are examples of this. Here a direct

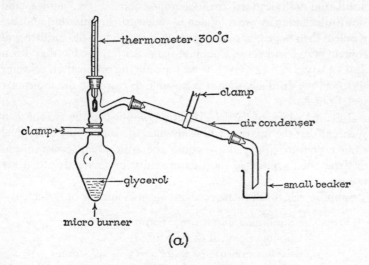

(a)

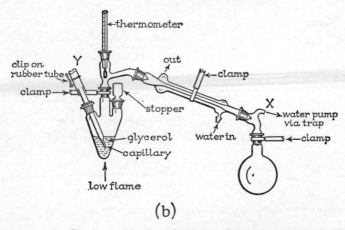

(b)

Fig. 9.—(a) The direct distillation of glycerol
(b) The vacuum distillation of glycerol

distillation will lead to the decomposition of the liquids, and steam distillation is used. Water is added to the mixture, and the whole is then boiled by blowing steam through it. The distillate will contain water and A, and because these are immiscible they form distinct layers in the receiver. If we measure the proportions of water and A in the distillate, then it is possible to calculate the molecular weight of A.

If Dalton's Law of Partial Pressures is applied to the system, it is apparent that the mixture will boil when the sum of the individual vapour pressures ($p_A + p_{H_2O}$) equals the atmospheric pressure, and that the boiling point of the mixture must be lower than that for water.

Suppose that the distillate contains a g of A and b g of water

> atmospheric pressure is P mm
> boiling point of the mixture is $T_1°$C
> vapour pressure of water at $T_1°$ is p_{H_2O} mm
> molecular weight of A is m

Then:

$$\frac{\text{weight of A}}{\text{weight of water}} = \frac{a}{b}$$

$$\frac{\text{molecules of A in distillate}}{\text{molecules of water in distillate}} = \frac{a/m}{b/18}$$

$$\therefore \frac{\text{molecules of A in vapour}}{\text{molecules of water in vapour}} = \frac{a/m}{b/18}$$

$$\therefore \frac{\text{vapour pressure of A at } T_1°\text{C}}{\text{vapour pressure of water at } T_1°\text{C}} = \frac{18a}{mb}$$

Now $P = p_{H_2O} + \text{vapour pressure of A}$

$$\therefore \frac{P - p_{H_2O}}{p_{H_2O}} = \frac{18a}{mb} \qquad (1)$$

The measured values may be substituted and m determined.

Numerical example

A plant oil was steam-distilled at 750 mm pressure and the mixture boiled at 98°C. The distillate contained 10 g of oil and 40 g of water. The vapour pressure of water at 98°C is 720 mm. What is the molecular weight of the oil?

$$\frac{750 - 720}{720} = \frac{18 \times 10}{m \times 40}$$

$$m = 108$$

Experiment 7. To determine the molecular weight of chlorobenzene

Set up the apparatus shown in fig. 10. The distilling flask B is three-necked, and the rubber tube connecting the flask B with the steam generator A must be as short as possible so that steam does not

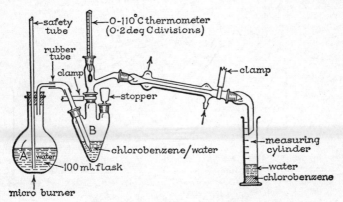

Fig. 10.—Steam distillation—small scale

condense unnecessarily. Place 5 ml of chlorobenzene and 5 ml of water in B. Heat A and B until the mixture begins to boil, and the water in the generator is boiling vigorously. Stop heating B, but continue with A. Collect the distillate in a small measuring cylinder (10 ml). Note the boiling point of the mixture using a thermometer reading to 110°C. When 3 ml of chlorobenzene have been collected, note the volume of water which has distilled in the same time.

Calculate the molecular weight of chlorobenzene by substituting the values of a, b, P, p_{H_2O} in equation (1). The values of a and b are obtained by multiplying the observed volumes by the respective densities. (Density of C_6H_5Cl is $1 \cdot 1$ g cm^{-3}.) List the errors associated with the method.

Experiment 8. The isolation of orange oil

A small-scale apparatus is inadequate for this experiment. To obtain appreciable yields, the isolation must be conducted on a kilogram of orange peel, and the apparatus shown in fig. 11 is suitable.

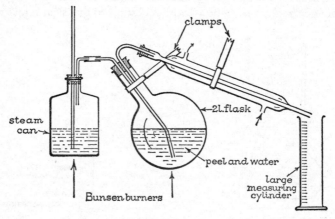

Fig. 11.—The isolation of orange oil

The peel is diced as finely as possible; it is bruised or (better still) pulped using a pestle and mortar, and then transferred to the 2-l flask. Water is added until the pulp is just covered and the mixture is then left overnight. The steam lead is inserted and the condenser attached. The mixture and the steam generator are heated, and the distillate is collected in a large measuring cylinder. When no more oil distils. it is separated from the water using a tap funnel.

C. ETHER EXTRACTION

When a sparingly soluble substance A must be separated from its mixture with a large volume of water, and A is known to be very soluble in ether, then the technique of ether extraction may be used for the isolation. Depending on the proportions of water and A, the mixture may be in one of a number of forms.

(*a*) A may be dissolved in the water and only one phase visible.

(*b*) A may form an emulsion in the saturated solution of A in water. Here, tiny globules of A are suspended in the aqueous phase. In such cases two layers may form, but the process might take a long time.

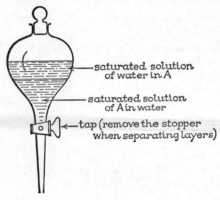

saturated solution of water in A

saturated solution of A in water

tap (remove the stopper when separating layers)

Fig. 12

(*c*) The mixture may form two layers, one a saturated solution of water in A, the other a saturated solution of A in water. In this case a separating funnel (fig. 12) may be used to collect the 'water in A layer'; this may then be dried using anhydrous calcium chloride. The water layer may contain worthwhile quantities of A and this is recovered by ether extraction.

When ether is added to these systems, then A distributes itself between the water and the ether layers, so that at equilibrium

$$\frac{\text{concentration of A in ether}}{\text{concentration of A in water}}$$

is constant (Distribution Ratio or Partition Coefficient). The efficiency of ether extraction depends on the value of the ratio, and this may be determined at a particular temperature by conducting independent experiments. If A has a large ratio, then the ether extraction will be speedy and efficient; most of A will dissolve in the ether.

The efficiency of extraction

One consequence of the behaviour of A when it becomes distributed between ether and water in contact, is that a given volume of ether is best applied in several independent extractions rather than all at once.

Suppose v ml of an aqueous solution contain w g of A, and that l ml of ether are added. At equilibrium, w_1 g of A remain in the water, then

concentration of A in water at equilibrium is w_1/v g ml^{-1}
concentration of A in ether at equilibrium is $(w - w_1)/l$ g ml^{-1}

These are related thus:

$$\frac{w_1/v}{(w - w_1)/l} = K$$

or
$$w_1 = \frac{wKv}{Kv + l}$$

If after a second extraction with l ml of ether, w_2 g of A remain in the water,

$$w_2 = \frac{w_1Kv}{Kv + l}$$

$$= w\left(\frac{Kv}{Kv + l}\right)^2$$

(H912)

After n extractions with l ml of ether, w_n g of A remain:

$$w_n = w\left(\frac{Kv}{Kv + l}\right)^n$$

If A is to be isolated using V ml of ether, then

$$nl = V \quad \text{or} \quad n = V/l$$

$$w_n = w\left(\frac{Kv}{Kv + l}\right)^{V/l} \qquad (2)$$

$$\frac{Kv}{Kv + l} < 1; \quad V/l > 1.$$

As l becomes smaller, w_n, the unextracted A, becomes smaller. The process is more efficient if it is conducted by repeated applications of smaller volumes of ether.

The number of extractions done is a compromise between the aims to recover as much A as possible, and to spend as little time as possible in doing it.

Why in isolating A from water do we set up the new problem of isolating it from ether? Because:

1. The volume of ether will be smaller.

2. The ether is volatile and may be easily evaporated.

3. The ether is inert and will not react with A.

One disadvantage of the solvent is that it presents a serious fire and explosion risk.

Numerical example

A solution of 10 g A in 100 ml water is shaken (*a*) with 100 ml ether, (*b*) with 5 lots of 20 ml ether. Calculate the efficiencies of the two processes Distribution Ratio of A between water and ether is $\frac{1}{5}$.

(H 912)

(*a*) Substitute in equation (2)

$$w = 10\,\text{g}$$
$$K = \tfrac{1}{5}$$
$$v = 100\,\text{ml}$$
$$l = 100\,\text{ml}$$
$$w_n = 10 \times \left(\frac{\tfrac{1}{5} \times 100}{\tfrac{1}{5} \times 100 + 100}\right)^{100/100}$$
$$w_n = 10 \times \left(\frac{20}{120}\right)^1$$
$$\simeq 1\cdot 6\,\text{g}$$

(*b*) Substitute in equation (2)

$$w = 10\,\text{g}$$
$$K = \tfrac{1}{5}$$
$$v = 100\,\text{ml}$$
$$l = 20\,\text{ml}$$
$$w_n = 10 \times \left(\frac{\tfrac{1}{5} \times 100}{\tfrac{1}{5} \times 100 + 20}\right)^{100/20}$$
$$w_n = 10 \times \left(\frac{1}{2}\right)^5$$
$$\simeq 0\cdot 30\,\text{g}$$

In case (*a*) the process is $\dfrac{8\cdot 4}{10} \times 100$ (84%) efficient.

In case (*b*) it is $\dfrac{9\cdot 7}{10} \times 100$ (97%) efficient.

Experiment 9. To study the efficiency of ether extraction (1)

CAUTION: *Ether is highly inflammable and forms explosive mixtures with air. Work with a minimum of equipment on the bench and avoid naked flames.*

Using a measuring cylinder, place 50 ml of bromine water in a separating funnel. Add 20 ml of ether, replace the stopper, and shake the mixture gently. At regular intervals invert the funnel and open the tap so as to reduce the pressure over the mixture. Set the funnel upright and allow the two layers to form. Transfer the aqueous layer into a clean boiling-tube by removing the stopper and controlling the transfer using the tap.

Now repeat the experiment, using 50 ml of the same bromine water, but this time extract twice with 10-ml portions of ether. Remove one portion before adding the second. Transfer the extracted aqueous layer to a boiling-tube. Compare the two solutions and judge the effectiveness of extraction by comparing the colours.

Experiment 10. Efficiency of ether extraction (2)

Place a few crystals of iodine in a flask, add 250 ml of distilled water, cork the flask, and shake it until the solution is saturated. Decant 100 ml of the solution into a measuring cylinder and then transfer it into a separating funnel. Add 50 ml of ether and extract the aqueous solution. Allow two layers to form. Place a small measuring cylinder under the funnel and run out 50 ml of the aqueous solution. Titrate this with ·001 N sodium thiosulphate from a burette, using starch as indicator. Note the volume of thiosulphate required.

Repeat the experiment using another 100 ml portion of the saturated iodine solution, this time extracting twice with 25 ml portions of ether, discarding the first before applying the second. Note the volume of thiosulphate required for 50 ml of the aqueous layer. Compare the efficiency of the two processes.

D. CHROMATOGRAPHIC SEPARATIONS

If two substances A and B are dissolved in a common solvent S, and the solution is made to travel through a stationary medium, then this medium will sometimes adsorb A and B to different extents. In this way A and B may be separated. The efficiency of the separation will depend upon several factors.

1. The nature of the stationary medium. Chalk, alumina, magnesium oxide, glucose, are a few in common use. Filter paper is often effective.
2. The nature of the solvent S. For a given stationary medium, some solvents will allow a clear separation of A and B, whilst others allow no resolution at all. Sometimes mixtures of solvents are used, sometimes different solvents are added in sequence.

When an adsorbent is in equilibrium with a solution of A/B in S, then at a particular temperature the following relations hold:

$$\frac{\text{quantity of A adsorbed}}{(\text{concentration of A in S})^{1/n_1}} = K_1$$

$$\frac{\text{quantity of B adsorbed}}{(\text{concentration of B in S})^{1/n_2}} = K_2$$

The efficiency of separation will depend upon the values of K_1 and n_1, K_2 and n_2, which are characteristic constants.

The chromatographic technique has many advantages. Very small quantities of A/B may be treated. Compared with other methods, it is very effective where A and B are chemically similar, or where A and B might be decomposed by processes involving heating them.

Method

In the following experiments, filter paper is used as the stationary medium. The paper is supported between two pieces of glass, 6 in × 6 in, one of which has a small hole bored through its centre. The mixture for separation is dissolved in some suitable solvent, and one drop of the mixed solution is placed at the centre of the paper using a capillary. The paper is allowed to dry by waving it in the hot air over a Bunsen flame. Cut the paper to the centre of the drop, making parallel cuts so that it may be arranged as in fig. 13. Place the paper between glass plates, so that the strip hangs through the hole in the bottom plate, and use clothes pegs to nip the plates together. Support the plates so that the 'tail' dips into a beaker containing the solvent S.

Experiment 11. The resolution of black ink

Use one drop of black ink, and water as the solvent S. Carefully record the sequence of coloured rings, and note that each of these is at least one chemical compound.

Experiment 12. The resolution of some plant pigments

Grind some grass cuttings in a mortar, transfer the pulp to a conical flask and add enough acetone to cover it. Place a filter funnel in the neck of the flask, set the whole on a water-bath, and allow the acetone to boil gently for a few minutes. Decant the green solution into an evaporating basin and concentrate it on the water-bath. Spot a paper with the concentrate, dry it, spot it again at the same place, dry it, and repeat this until there is a heavy stain at the centre of the paper. Resolve the mixture using acetone as the solvent S. Record the sequence of rings.

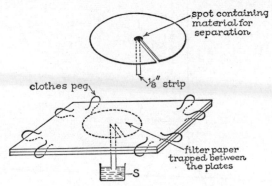

Fig. 13.—Chromatographic separations

Experiment 13. The resolution of screened methyl orange

Spot the paper with screened methyl orange, dry it, spot it again until there is a heavy stain at the centre. Resolve the mixture using water as the solvent. When there is a clear separation of colours, dry the paper. Spot the orange band with acid, then with alkali.

Observe that the response is typical of methyl orange. Examine the blue band in a similar way.

Column chromatography

Experiment 14. The separation of fluorescein and methylene blue

The apparatus is shown in fig. 14. The column may be made from the tap end of a burette and should be about 12 in long. The narrow end is heated in a Bunsen flame until the constriction is narrowed

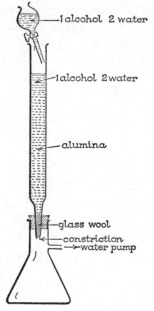

1 alcohol 2 water

1 alcohol 2 water

alumina

glass wool

constriction

water pump

Fig. 14.—Column chromatography

considerably. Make a plug of glass wool and push this to the narrow end of the tube using a glass rod. When the 'wool' is firmly in place, stop the narrow end of the tube with a teat, set the column in the flask as shown, and half-fill the tube with industrial methylated spirit. Add alumina (chromatographic quality) to the tube, tapping the tube with a piece of pressure tube to ensure that the alumina falls to form a uniform column. Continue the addition until the column is about 6 in long. Remove the teat and replace the column on the Büchner flask. Attach the flask to a water-pump, and maintain a 'vacuum' which causes the alcohol to drip through at a rate of one drop a second. When the alcohol has fallen to half an inch of the alumina level, stop the vacuum. (IT IS IMPORTANT THAT NO PART OF THE COLUMN SHOULD DRY OUT.) Make a solution of a few crystals of methylene blue and a similar quantity of fluorescein in 5 ml of alcohol, and slowly transfer the solution into the tube, being careful not to disturb the surface of the alumina. Allow the dyes to move into the column for about five minutes without applying a vacuum. Now apply a vacuum and keep the column covered by running in industrial alcohol from the tap funnel. Continue until all the methylene blue has been transferred to the flask. Stop the vacuum and transfer the methylene blue solution to a beaker. Clean the flask and reset the column. Now draw water through the column and collect the aqueous solution of fluorescein.

The Purification of Substances by Chemical Techniques

4

Sometimes the ingredients of a mixture may be separated by the addition of a reagent which reacts with one component only. If one component is acidic (HA) and the other is basic (B), then separation may be obtained by dissolving the mixture in ether, and then washing the ether with a solution of sodium hydroxide (Na^+OH^-). The reaction occurs:

$$HA + OH^- \rightarrow H_2O + A^-$$

and Na^+A^- will concentrate in the aqueous layer. This layer may be removed and the acid recovered by adding a mineral acid:

$$A^- + H^+ \rightarrow HA$$

If HA is insoluble in water, isolation is easy: it may be filtered if it is a solid; if it is liquid, a separating funnel may be used. If HA is sparingly soluble in water, then it may be isolated by ether extraction.

The base remains in the ether and may be washed out by the addition of a mineral acid:

$$B + H^+ \rightarrow BH^+$$

The acid washings may now be treated with alkali, and the free base liberated:

$$BH^+ + OH^- \rightarrow B + H_2O$$

If one component of the mixture will undergo addition reactions and the other will not, then separation might follow the pattern:

1. A/B + addition reactant R $\rightarrow$ AR + B
2. Filter to retain AR.
3. Decompose AR to obtain A.

Experiment 15. To isolate the acids and alkalis from coal tar

CAUTION: *The coal tar must not come in contact with the skin. The process involves the use of ether. Avoid naked flames.*

The composition of coal tar depends upon the type of coal used in its manufacture, and also upon the working temperature of the retorts. The treatment of the tar is not uniform throughout industry; there is much variation of detail, but basically it is distilled into several fractions, and the most volatile fraction is called the *light oil*. This contains benzene C_6H_6, toluene $C_6H_5 . CH_3$, and other hydrocarbons; phenol C_6H_5OH, cresol $C_6H_4 . CH_3 . OH$, and other acidic compounds; pyridine C_5H_5N, and other bases.

Place 20 ml of light oil in a separating funnel and add 50 ml of ether. Swirl the funnel until mixing is complete. Add 50 ml of bench sodium hydroxide and shake the mixture for several minutes (1), inverting the funnel and opening the tap at intervals. Allow two layers to form and run the aqueous layer into a beaker. Stir the alkali washings and add concentrated hydrochloric acid *slowly*; continue the addition until the solution is acid (2). Observe the formation of free acids and the strong smell of phenol.

Next shake the ether solution with dilute sulphuric acid (3), isolate the acid washings, and make them alkaline with sodium hydroxide solution (4). Detect the presence of pyridine by its characteristic unpleasant smell. Hydrocarbons remain in the ether.

(1) $$C_6H_5OH + OH^- \rightarrow \underset{\text{phenate}}{C_6H_5O^-} + H_2O$$

(2) $$C_6H_5O^- + H^+ \rightarrow C_6H_5OH \quad \text{(free acid)}$$

(3) $$C_5H_5N + H^+ \rightarrow C_5H_5N^+H$$

(4) $$C_5H_5N^+H + OH^- \rightarrow C_5H_5N + H_2O$$

If light oil is not available, then the separation can be carried out using a mixture of phenol, aniline, and benzene. Prepare the mixture in a test-tube and use the method described. Aniline is a base $C_6H_5NH_2$.

Experiment 16. To separate benzaldehyde from benzene

CAUTION: *Ether is used; avoid naked flames.*

Mix a little benzaldehyde and benzene in a test-tube (1 ml of each). Add a saturated solution of sodium bisulphite to the mixture, cork the tube, and shake it vigorously. Note that the formation of benzaldehyde sodium bisulphite crystals is accompanied by the evolution of heat.

$$C_6H_5.CHO + Na^+HSO_3^- \rightarrow (C_6H_5CHO.SO_3H)^-Na^+$$

Allow the tube to cool and filter off the solid using a Büchner flask and funnel.

Solid.—Wash this with a little ether, transfer it to a beaker and add a slight excess of sodium carbonate solution; stir thoroughly. When the evolution of gas is complete, transfer the contents of the beaker to a separating funnel and ether-extract the benzaldehyde (see Experiment 9). Dry the ethereal solution of benzaldehyde with anhydrous calcium chloride. Decant the dry solution into a dish and evaporate the ether ON A WATER-BATH IN A FUME CUPBOARD. Benzaldehyde remains.

Solution.—Ether-extract the solution to obtain benzene. Collect the ether layer in a small flask. Add a few grains of anhydrous calcium chloride to dry the solution, and leave it stoppered for $\frac{1}{2}$ h. Decant the dry solution into a distillation apparatus (fig. 4). Distil the mixture on a water-bath, collecting the fraction which boils at 75–85°C, discarding the rest.

Detection of the Elements in Organic Compounds

5

Experiment 17. To detect carbon and hydrogen

(i) Mix 1 g of glucose and 1 g of *dry* copper oxide in a clean dry test-tube. Fit a delivery tube as shown in fig. 15. Heat the mixture gently and pass any gases evolved into lime-water. Observe the water condensing in the delivery tube—this indicates the presence of hydrogen in the glucose. Observe the formation of copper on the walls of the test-tube.

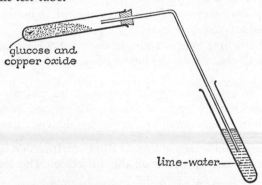

glucose and copper oxide

lime-water

Fig. 15.—The detection of carbon and hydrogen

(ii) Pour a few drops of benzene into a crucible and ignite it. Observe the carbon content of the flame. A sooty flame is characteristic of compounds containing a high percentage of carbon, but it must be remembered that in a limited supply of air, any carbon compound will burn with a sooty flame.

Experiment 18. The detection of metals

If an organic compound is very strongly heated in an oxidizing atmosphere, a permanent residue (ash) indicates the presence of a

33

metal. The ash will be the oxide or the carbonate of the metal, and after it has cooled it may be studied by the usual method of group separations.

1. Place a little calcium acetate on a crucible lid, set this on a pipe-clay triangle, and heat it strongly for several minutes, using a direct Bunsen flame. Allow the lid to cool, moisten the residue with concentrated hydrochloric acid, and do a flame test on the paste.

2. Repeat the experiment with sodium acetate.

3. Repeat the experiment with a small piece of soap.

Experiment 19. The detection of nitrogen

1. Place a few crystals of acetamide in a test-tube. Add bench sodium hydroxide and warm the mixture. Test the gases evolved with damp red litmus paper. The evolution of ammonia indicates that acetamide is nitrogenous.

. 2. Add soda lime to a little urea in a test-tube. Heat the mixture strongly and observe the evolution of ammonia. Urea is nitrogenous.

3. Add concentrated sodium hydroxide to aniline, boil the mixture, and test the gases evolved for the presence of ammonia. Aniline is nitrogenous but this particular test does not detect it.

Whether alkali liberates ammonia from a nitrogenous compound depends upon the structure of the molecule. The linkages in acetamide and urea are

$$R—\underset{\underset{O}{\|}}{C}—NH_2 \quad \text{and} \quad NH_2—\underset{\underset{O}{\|}}{C}—NH_2$$

respectively, and these will give ammonia. The linkage in aniline is $R—NH_2$, and this will not provide ammonia.

Experiment 20. The detection of halogens

1. Add a few drops of chloroform ($CHCl_3$), carbon tetrachloride, and ethyl bromide to separate portions of silver nitrate

solution. Observe that the silver halides are *not* formed immediately.

2. Make a solution of aniline hydrochloride, add silver nitrate solution, and observe the immediate formation of silver chloride.

The negative tests 1 are due to the chemical linkages being covalent in character. Chloroform, carbon tetrachloride, and ethyl bromide have structures

$$\begin{matrix} & \text{Cl} & & & \text{Cl} & & & \text{H} & \text{H} \\ & | & & & | & & & | & | \\ \text{H}-\text{C}-\text{Cl} & & \text{Cl}-\text{C}-\text{Cl} & & \text{H}-\text{C}-\text{C}-\text{Br} \\ & | & & & | & & & | & | \\ & \text{Cl} & & & \text{Cl} & & & \text{H} & \text{H} \end{matrix}$$

Aniline hydrochloride is an ionic compound $(C_6H_5NH_3)^+Cl^-$.

3. Take a piece of thick copper wire and heat one end of it in a Bunsen flame until the flame is no longer coloured green. Allow the wire to cool a little but, whilst still hot, place it in a little chloroform. Heat the wire again and observe the green-blue flame. This indicates that chloroform contains a halogen.

Experiment 21. The detection of halogens, sulphur, nitrogen, using a fusion mixture

The fusion mixture disrupts the compound under investigation, covalent linkages are broken, and ions are produced:

$$\begin{aligned} {>}S &\rightarrow S^{--} \\ -Cl &\rightarrow Cl^- \\ -Br &\rightarrow Br^- \\ -I &\rightarrow I^- \\ \underset{|}{\overset{|}{-C}}{\diagdown}_{N-} &\rightarrow CN^- \end{aligned}$$

Tests are then conducted on an aqueous solution of the anions.

The preparation of the fusion mixture (Middleton's method)

25 g of pure sodium carbonate are weighed out and transferred to a clean dry mortar. 50 g of pure zinc powder are added, and the two are ground together thoroughly. The mixture is stored in a clean dry reagent bottle ready for use.

The fusion

The technique depends upon the substance under investigation.

Solids.—Place 0·2–0·5 g in a small hard-glass test-tube. Add fusion mixture to a depth of half an inch. Shake the tube until the contents are thoroughly mixed. Add more fusion mixture to a depth of one inch.

Liquids.—Place fusion mixture in a tube to a depth of half an inch. Add three or four drops of the liquid under test. Now add more fusion mixture to a depth of 1·5 in.

The heating

Grasp the tube using a test-tube holder. Adjust a Bunsen burner to give a low flame and heat the mixture at the open end of the tube, holding the tube horizontally. Slowly increase the size of the flame until the mixture at the open end is red hot. Continue to heat the whole mixture. Finally heat the tube when it is held vertically.

The solution

Place 50 ml of distilled water in a clean mortar. Whilst the test-tube is still red hot, immerse the end in the water. Crush the mixture and the glass so that solution is efficient. Filter the solution and preserve the residue and the filtrate.

The test for sulphur

Any sulphur will be in the residue as zinc sulphide. Place the residue in an evaporating dish and add dilute hydrochloric acid. Moisten a filter paper with lead acetate solution and place this over the dish. A blackening indicates the presence of sulphur in the substance.

$$S^{--} + 2H^+ \rightarrow H_2S$$

The test for halogens

Acidify a portion of the filtrate with dilute nitric acid, boil it for several minutes, and then add silver nitrate solution. A precipitate indicates halogen. Now add dilute ammonia until the solution is alkaline.

Precipitate insoluble in ammonia — IODIDE
slowly soluble   — BROMIDE
immediately soluble   — CHLORIDE.

Acidify another portion of the filtrate with dilute sulphuric acid, boil it for a short time, and then allow it to cool. Add 2–3 ml of carbon tetrachloride to the solution and then add chlorine water dropwise. After each addition shake the tube. A violet colour in the carbon tetrachloride layer indicates *iodine* (1). Continue the addition of chlorine water until the violet fades (2). Further addition of chlorine water causes the layer to go brown if *bromine* is present (3).

1. $2I^- + Cl_2 \rightarrow I_2 + 2Cl^-$
2. $I_2 + 6H_2O + 5Cl_2 \rightarrow 2IO_3^- + 12H^+ + 10Cl^-$
3. $2Br^- + Cl_2 \rightarrow Br_2 + 2Cl^-$

An alternative method of fusion (The Lassaigne sodium test)

CAUTION: Great care must be exercised in carrying out this test. There is a risk of explosion, and the possibility that molten sodium will spurt from the tube. It is best to work the fusion in a fume cupboard, otherwise the wearing of goggles is advised.

The fusion

Place about 0·2 g of the organic compound in a small hard-glass test-tube. Introduce three small pieces of sodium (up to 5 mm in diameter) having blotted them free of oil. Take the tube in a holder and gently heat the mixture over a Bunsen flame. BE CAREFUL WHERE YOU POINT THE TUBE. Now heat the tube strongly until the glass begins to soften.

The solution

Still grasping the tube in its holder, plunge the hot end into 50 ml of distilled water in a mortar. Crush the glass and the mixture with a pestle, filter, and treat the filtrate as described already (page 37).

An alternative test for sulphide

In the Lassaigne fusion, all sulphur is converted to sodium sulphide, and this will be present in the filtrate. It may be detected by adding a freshly prepared solution of sodium nitroprusside ($Na_2[Fe(CN)_5 . NO]2H_2O$) to a portion of the filtrate. A purple coloration indicates the presence of sulphur

Nitrogen

Take a second portion of the filtrate, add a few drops of sodium hydroxide solution, follow this with a little ferrous sulphate solution. Boil the mixture, allow it to cool, and then acidify it with concentrated hydrochloric acid. A blue coloration indicates the presence of nitrogen in the substance under investigation. (Sometimes the blue coloration is made clearer if the solution is filtered. The blue residue is Prussian blue, and has the constitution, $K^+Fe^{++}[Fe(CN)_6]^{3-}nH_2O$.)

Use the fusion method to detect which elements are present in

(a) sulphanilic acid
(b) aniline hydrochloride
(c) piece of fingernail
(d) a few strands of hair.

Quantitative Analysis

6

After finding which elements are present in a compound, the percentage composition is investigated. It is necessary to know this if an empirical formula is to be assigned to the compound. If a compound contains $x\%$C, $y\%$H, and $z\%$Cl, where $x + y + z = 100$, then we can say:

1. The qualitative analysis is complete.
2. The molecule of the substance contains atoms in the ratio

$$\text{C} : \text{H} : \text{Cl} = \frac{x}{12} : \frac{y}{1} : \frac{z}{35 \cdot 5}$$

The actual number of atoms present in a molecule can be determined only by molecular weight measurement.

The quantitative analysis of carbon, hydrogen, halogens, and sulphur demands equipment rarely available in teaching laboratories. The methods used for the work depend upon the constitution of the substance under investigation; if carbon is to be determined, the method used will depend upon which other elements are present. If, for example, nitrogen is known to be present, then an appropriate modification is used.

Experiment 22. To determine the percentage of nitrogen in acetanilide (Kjeldahl method)

A known weight of acetanilide is heated with concentrated sulphuric acid and potassium sulphate. (This to elevate the boiling point of the acid.) Under these conditions the nitrogen forms ammonium sulphate. The solution is then made alkaline, and ammonia is distilled into standard acid. The ammonia is determined by titration.

This method has a limited application. It gives poor results for compounds where chemical linkages prevent the easy conversion of nitrogen into ammonium ions. Such linkages occur in nitro compounds $N{<}{\overset{O}{\underset{\searrow O}{}}}$; azo compounds —N=N—; hydrazones =N—N—.

Method

1. Weigh a stoppered bottle containing about 0·5 g of acetanilide.

2. Transfer the solid into a round-bottomed flask (1 litre). The flask must be perfectly dry so that all the solid falls into the bulb. Reweigh the bottle and calculate the weight of acetanilide transferred.

3. Pour 20 ml of concentrated sulphuric acid into the flask and swirl it round so that all the solid becomes moistened with the acid.

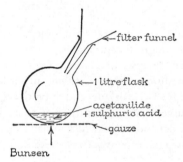

Fig. 16.—The Kjeldahl method for nitrogen

4. Clamp the flask as shown in fig. 16. Place a filter funnel in the neck of the flask and heat it gently over a Bunsen burner for half an hour. The heating must be done in a fume cupboard because sulphur dioxide is produced. Care must be taken to see that materials are not lost due to the frothing which might occur.

5. Allow the flask to cool a little and add about 10 g of dry powdered potassium sulphate. Reheat the flask until the contents are

boiling gently. Continue the heating until the contents of the flask are clear and pale yellow in colour (about 3 h).

6. Set up the apparatus shown in fig. 17.

7. Disconnect the litre flask A, and introduce about 100 ml of distilled water and a few drops of methyl orange.

8. Carefully pour the clear acid solution into A, wash out the flask used in stages 1–5, and pour the wash water into A. Now reassemble the apparatus.

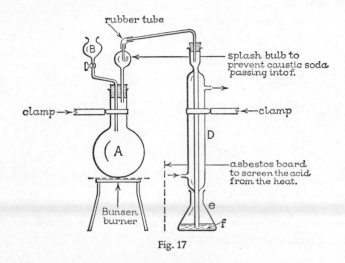

Fig. 17

9. Pipette 50 ml of normal hydrochloric acid into the conical flask e, and arrange the tip of the condenser so that it is just beneath the surface of the acid.

10. Put 30% sodium hydroxide solution into the funnel B, and run the alkali into A until the contents are alkaline. (The methyl orange will now be yellow.)

11. Warm A so that ammonia is evolved. As the ammonia is absorbed in the acid f, the acid will rise up the condenser and will fall back periodically. Add more alkali via B at intervals, and slowly

bring the solution in A to the boil. When the boiling solution is permanently alkaline, continue boiling it for 15 minutes.

12. Disconnect the condenser and raise it clear of f. Wash it through with distilled water and rinse the tip, collecting the wash water in e.

13. Add a few drops of methyl orange to e and titrate the contents with normal sodium hydroxide.

Calculation

Weight of acetanilide is x g

50 ml normal HCl at the start

v ml normal NaOH used for titration

Ammonia $\equiv (50 - v)$ ml normal HCl

$\therefore$ The compound contains $\dfrac{(50 - v) \times 14}{1000}$ g nitrogen

$\therefore$ The percentage of nitrogen is $\dfrac{(50 - v) \times 14}{10x}$

Compare your result with that obtained by calculation from the formula for acetanilide, C_8H_9ON.

The percentage nitrogen in a foodstuff or in a fertilizer may be determined using the method. Bone meal or gelatin are convenient, and 2 g samples should be analysed.

Experiment 23. To determine the number of amino groups in aniline

When a primary amine is heated with a mixture of acetic anhydride and glacial acetic acid then the amine is acetylated:

$$R(NH_2)_x + x(CH_3CO)_2O \rightarrow R(NH.CO.CH_3)_x + xCH_3.COOH$$

The excess acetic anhydride is then hydrolysed by boiling the mixture with water, and the acetic acid produced is determined by titration with sodium hydroxide solution. A control experiment is conducted, omitting the amine. The results of the two experiments are compared in order to calculate the number of amino groups.

Method

Fit two conical flasks A and B with air condensers, making the attachment with rubber stoppers. Both flasks must be clean and dry. Weigh flask A and introduce about 1·5 ml of aniline; reweigh the flask. Prepare the acetylating mixture by shaking together 13 ml of acetic anhydride and 7 ml of glacial acetic acid. Transfer the mixture to a clean dry burette and run 4·0 ml into flask A. Add the same volume of the acetylating mixture to flask B. Set the air condensers in position and heat A and B on a boiling water-bath for half an hour (fig. 18).

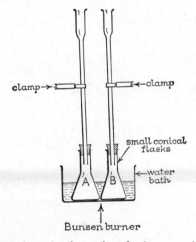

Fig. 18.—To determine the number of amino groups in aniline

Pour 50 ml of hot water into each flask via the condensers, and continue the heating for 10 min more. Remove the flasks and allow them to cool down, loosen the condensers, and rinse both the outside tips and the insides with cold water, collecting the wash water in the conical flasks. Titrate the contents of each with normal sodium hydroxide using phenolphthalein as the indicator.

Calculation

Weight of the aniline is x g.

The molecular weight is 93.

Volume of normal NaOH required for A is v_A ml.

Volume of normal NaOH required for B is v_B ml.

$\dfrac{(v_B - v_A)}{1000}$ g mol of acetic acid have been used by the aniline.

$\therefore \dfrac{v_B - v_A}{1000}$ amino groups present.

But $\dfrac{x}{93}$ g mol of aniline were used.

$\therefore$ One molecule of aniline contains $\dfrac{(v_B - v_A) \times 93}{1000x}$ NH$_2$ groups.

Aniline has the formula $C_6H_5 . NH_2$.

Reduction Reactions

7

An ordinary chemical equation conveys information. It explains that a particular chemical change will occur, and it describes reacting weights and the weights of the products which will be obtained. On the other hand it is of little help in showing the wider significance of the reaction; general implications are not made clear.

If each reactant and product is represented by its structural formula, then a wider meaning becomes apparent.

1. $$Na_2CO_3 + 2HCl \rightarrow 2NaCl + H_2O + CO_2$$

2. $$2Na^+ + CO_3^{--} + 2H^+ + 2Cl^- \rightarrow 2Na^+ + 2Cl^-$$
$$+ \underset{\text{covalent}}{H_2O} + \underset{\text{covalent}}{CO_2}$$

Sodium ions and chloride ions are unchanged in this process. They are not reactants so that we can leave them out of the equation. This then becomes:

3. $$CO_3^{--} + 2H^+ \rightarrow H_2O + CO_2$$

Equation 3 is an *ionic equation* which explains that *any* carbonate will react with *any* strong acid to produce carbon dioxide and water—*provided that the reactants may come in contact.* In an ionic equation there must be a balance of charges. In equation 3 the reactants together have no charge, and the same must be true of the products.

When sodium hydroxide neutralizes nitric acid, then the reaction may be represented as

$$NaOH + HNO_3 \rightarrow NaNO_3 + H_2O$$

structurally $Na^+OH^- + H^+NO_3^- \rightarrow Na^+NO_3^- + H_2O$ (covalent) ionic equation $OH^- + H^+ \rightarrow H_2O$

Here again, the wider implication of neutralization is made clear.

If ionic equations are written for oxidation–reduction (redox) reactions, then the general nature of oxidation–reduction is apparent.

Example 1

The oxidation of zinc to zinc oxide.

$$2Zn + O_2 \rightarrow 2ZnO$$

ionically $2Zn + O_2 \rightarrow 2Zn^{++} + 2O^{--}$

Here electrons have been provided by zinc atoms and they have been accepted by oxygen atoms. The two processes may be represented using the symbol e to represent an electron.

$$2Zn \rightarrow 2Zn^{++} + 4e \text{ (oxidation of zinc)}$$
$$4e + O_2 \rightarrow 2O^{--} \qquad \text{(reduction of oxygen)}$$

Example 2

The oxidation of ferrous chloride to ferric chloride by chlorine.

$$2FeCl_2 + Cl_2 \rightarrow 2FeCl_3$$

ionically $2Fe^{++} + 4Cl^- + Cl_2 \rightarrow 2Fe^{3+} + 6Cl^-$

The fundamental processes are:

$$2Fe^{++} \rightarrow 2Fe^{3+} + 2e \text{ (oxidation of ferrous)}$$
$$2e + Cl_2 \rightarrow 2Cl^- \qquad \text{(reduction of chlorine)}$$

Example 3

The reduction of copper oxide by hydrogen gas.

$$CuO + H_2 \rightarrow Cu + H_2O$$

ionically $Cu^{++}O^{--} + H_2 \rightarrow Cu + H_2O$

The fundamental processes:

$$Cu^{++} + 2e \rightarrow Cu \qquad \text{(reduction of cupric ion)}$$
$$(O^{--} + H_2) - 2e \rightarrow H_2O \quad \text{(oxidation of the } O^{--}/H_2 \text{ system)}$$

When electrons are removed from a system then the system is said to be *oxidized*. When a system accepts electrons then it is an *oxidizing agent*. *Reduction* is the addition of electrons to a system, a *reducing agent* provides electrons.

Some common reducing agents

It is useful to classify these into acid, alkaline, and neutral systems.

A. acid

(i) Tin and hydrochloric acid
$$Sn \rightarrow Sn^{4+} + 4e$$

(ii) Stannous chloride in hydrochloric acid
$$Sn^{2+} \rightarrow Sn^{4+} + 2e$$

(iii) Hydriodic acid
$$2HI \rightarrow I_2 + 2H^+ + 2e$$

(iv) Hydrogen sulphide
$$H_2S \rightarrow 2H^+ + S + 2e$$

B. alkaline

(i) Zinc dust and sodium hydroxide
$$Zn + 2H_2O \rightarrow ZnO_2^{--} + 4H^+ + 2e$$
$$\text{zincate ion}$$

(ii) Sodium amalgam and water
$$Na \rightarrow Na^+ + e$$

C. neutral systems

Aluminium-mercury couple with methanol
$$Al \rightarrow Al^{3+} + 3e$$

The influence of conditions on the process of reduction

Conditions influence the rate of a reduction but, more important, they may determine the nature of the products formed. The diagram shows some of the products which may be obtained by the reduction of nitrobenzene

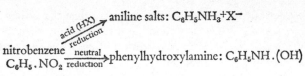

aniline salts: $C_6H_5NH_3^+X^-$

nitrobenzene $\xrightarrow{\text{neutral reduction}}$ phenylhydroxylamine: $C_6H_5NH.(OH)$
$C_6H_5.NO_2$

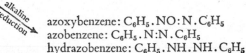

azoxybenzene: $C_6H_5.NO:N.C_6H_5$
azobenzene: $C_6H_5.N:N.C_6H_5$
hydrazobenzene: $C_6H_5.NH.NH.C_6H_5$

The duration of reduction may determine which product is formed. Hydrogen sulphide is a mild reducing agent, and it may be used for the partial reduction of meta dinitrobenzene by limiting its application. More powerful reducing agents would bring about complete reduction to form meta phenylene diamine—$C_6H_4(NH_2)_2$.

$$C_6H_4(NO_2)_2 \xrightarrow{(H_2S)} C_6H_4(NO_2)(NH_2) \quad \text{(meta nitraniline)}$$

Experiment 24. The reduction of phenol to benzene

The phenols are a class of aromatic compounds which contain at least one hydroxyl group linked directly to a benzene nucleus. A few common ones are represented below:

phenol   cresol   hydroquinone   pyrogallol
$C_6H_5.OH$ $CH_3.C_6H_4.OH$ $C_6H_4(OH)_2$ $C_6H_3(OH)_3$

The dry distillation of many naturally occurring substances, e.g. coal, wood, produces phenolic substances, and for this reason they are often encountered by chemists studying 'natural products'. When phenols are reduced with zinc dust, hydrocarbons are formed, and the process may be represented by

$$Zn \rightarrow Zn^{++} + 2e \quad \text{(oxidation)}$$
$$C_6H_5OH + 2e \rightarrow C_6H_6 + O^{--} \quad \text{(reduction)}$$

The significance of the reduction is that if the hydrocarbon is recognized, then the nature of the phenol is understood, and some insight is gained into the nature of the natural product.

Method

CAUTION: *Perform this reaction in a fume cupboard; failing this, wear goggles. Avoid getting phenol on the skin.*

Place a little phenol in a dry hard-glass test-tube (fig. 19). Now pack the tube loosely with asbestos impregnated with zinc dust. Set a delivery tube in the mouth of the test-tube, and place a boiling-tube containing sodium hydroxide solution at the open end of the

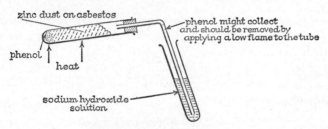

Fig. 19.—The reduction of phenol

delivery tube. Heat the asbestos strongly and, when it is very hot, heat the phenol crystals so that phenol vapour passes over the hot zinc. Continue heating the asbestos and the phenol until no more bubbles escape into the sodium hydroxide solution, then immediately disconnect the delivery tube.

CAUTION. A little phenol might collect in the delivery tube causing a blockage. The solid can be removed by fanning the tube with a small flame, but do not stop heating the asbestos whilst doing this, otherwise a 'suck back' will occur.

Smell the collecting tube to detect benzene, and ether-extract the alkaline solution to isolate the hydrocarbon. (CAUTION: See pages 24–25.) Acidify the sodium hydroxide solution and note the liberation of phenol. The method of reduction is inefficient.

Phenols are acidic, they dissolve in alkalis:

$$C_6H_5OH + OH^- \rightarrow C_6H_5O^- + H_2O$$

Acidification causes the reversal:

$$C_6H_5O^- + H^+ \rightarrow C_6H_5OH$$

Experiment 25. The reduction of methyl iodide to form methane

When clean aluminium is placed in mercuric chloride solution, a displacement reaction occurs:

$$2Al + 3Hg^{2+} \rightarrow 2Al^{3+} + 3Hg$$

The mercury displaced forms a layer on the aluminium surface and aluminium dissolves in this. The surface of the mercury may now provide aluminium atoms with great efficiency, as no film of aluminium oxide is present to inhibit the reactivity. When the metal couple is in contact with methyl alcohol and methyl iodide, the following processes occur:

$$2Al \rightarrow 2Al^{3+} + 6e \quad \text{(oxidation)}$$
$$6CH_3OH + 3CH_3I \rightarrow 6CH_3O^- + 3HI + 3CH_4 - 6e \text{ (reduction)}$$
$$\text{methoxide}$$

Overall, the reaction may be represented by

$$6CH_3OH + 3CH_3I + 2Al \rightarrow 2Al(OCH_3)_3 + 3HI + 3CH_4$$

Method

Place a few pieces of aluminium foil in a small conical flask. Cover them with mercuric chloride solution, and observe the displacement of mercury. After two minutes decant off the solution, and wash the couple with two lots of water and then two lots of methyl alcohol, discarding the wash liquids in each case. Cover the couple with methyl alcohol. The apparatus shown in fig. 20 is set up and methyl iodide is added dropwise into the reducing system. The methane gas is collected by displacement of water.

1. Ignite a tube of the gas and note the characteristics of the flame.

2. Pour a little bromine water into another tube of the gas, shake it, observe any change in colour.

3. Add a few drops of potassium permanganate made alkaline with sodium hydroxide solution to a third tube, shake, note any change in colour. [See these reactions for ethylene.]

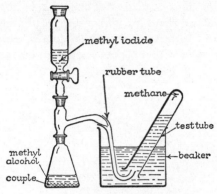

Fig. 20.—The reduction of methyl iodide

Experiment 26. Reduction of methyl iodide using a copper/zinc couple

The apparatus shown in fig. 20 is used. Granulated zinc is placed in the flask, and copper sulphate solution is added to cover the zinc. When the zinc is copper-covered, decant off the solution. Wash the couple with water, then with methyl alcohol; finally cover it with methyl alcohol and continue as in the last experiment. The production of methane is aided if the methyl alcohol is slightly acidified with two drops of dilute sulphuric acid.

Experiment 27. The reduction of nitrobenzene to form aniline

$$2C_6H_5NO_2 + 14H^+ \rightarrow 2C_6H_5NH_3^+ + 4H_2O - 12e$$

$$3Sn \rightarrow 3Sn^{4+} \qquad\qquad + 12e$$

Overall:

$$2C_6H_5NO_2 + 14HCl + 3Sn \rightarrow 2C_6H_5NH_3Cl + 3SnCl_4 + 4H_2O$$
$$\text{aniline hydrochloride}$$

When aniline hydrochloride is treated with an alkali, the free base is obtained:

$$C_6H_5 . NH_3^+ + OH^- \rightarrow C_6H_5NH_2 + H_2O$$

Method

Place 2 ml of nitrobenzene and 4·5 g of granulated tin in a three-necked flask. Attach a condenser at one neck, a dropping funnel at the second, and seal the third with a stopper (fig. 21a). Place 10 ml of concentrated hydrochloric acid in the funnel, and add this to the flask slowly. If the reaction becomes too vigorous, cool the flask by

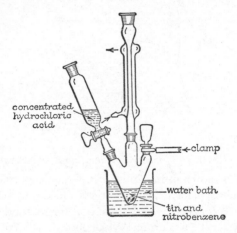

concentrated hydrochloric acid

←clamp

water bath

tin and nitrobenzene

Fig. 21.—The preparation of aniline
(a) Reflux stage

setting a beaker of cold water round it. When the addition is complete, heat the flask under reflux on a water-bath for 10 min. Convert the flask for steam distillation (fig. 21b) and add pellets of sodium hydroxide until the solution is alkaline. CAUTION: *The reaction is very exothermic. Add the pellets one at a time and make no more addition until the reaction has subsided.* Steam-distil the mixture until the distillate is free from aniline. Ether-extract the distillate with

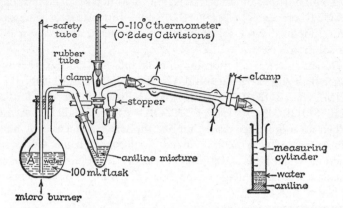

Fig. 21.—The preparation of aniline
(b) Steam distillation stage

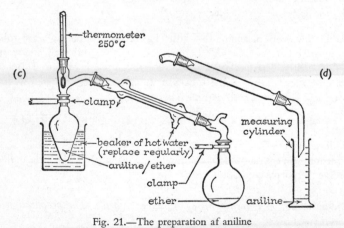

Fig. 21.—The preparation af aniline
(c) Removal of the ether (FUME CUPBOARD—
NO NAKED FLAME)

(d) Final distillation. Substitute an air condenser.
Heat the flask directly

two 5 ml portions of ether, collecting them in a small conical flask. CAUTION: *Avoid naked flames.* Add a few flakes of potassium hydroxide to dry the solution, stopper the flask, and leave it until the solution is clear.

Decant the clear solution into a flask and distil off the ether on a water-bath (fig. 21c). CONDUCT THE DISTILLATION IN A FUME CUPBOARD, USING A BEAKER OF HOT WATER AS THE SOURCE OF HEAT. AVOID ALL NAKED FLAMES. When no more ether distils, replace the water condenser by an air condenser, and heat the flask directly with a small flame. Collect the fraction which boils at 180–183°C. Record the yield of aniline and calculate what percentage of the theoretical value this represents.

Test-tube reactions of aniline

1. Conversion to diazonium salt and the condensations to form dyes (Experiment 41)
2. Acetylation (Experiment 46)
3. Action of bromine water (Experiment 74)
4. *The isocyanide reaction* (carbylamine)

Add a few drops of aniline to a little chloroform ($CHCl_3$) in a test-tube. Introduce 2 ml of alcoholic sodium hydroxide solution, mix well, and warm the tube gently. The unpleasant smell of carbylamine is produced. Before discarding the contents of the tube add an excess of concentrated hydrochloric acid so that the carbylamine is destroyed.

$$CHCl_3 + C_6H_5NH_2 + 3KOH \rightarrow C_6H_5NC + 3KCl + 3H_2O$$

5. *Bleaching powder*
Prepare a suspension of bleaching powder in water and add a little aniline. Observe the purple coloration.

Experiment 28. A reduction using stannous chloride. The preparation of phenylhydrazine

When sodium nitrite and hydrochloric acid react, then nitrous acid is produced (1). If this is allowed to react with an aniline salt at low temperatures then a diazonium salt is formed (2). Diazonium salts may be reduced by stannous chloride to form phenylhydrazine salts (3), from which phenylhydrazine is obtained by the addition of alkalis.

1. $$H^+ + NO_2^- \rightarrow HNO_2$$

2. $$C_6H_5NH_3^+ + HNO_2 \rightarrow C_6H_5N_2^+ + 2H_2O$$

3. $$\begin{cases} 2Sn^{2+} \rightarrow 2Sn^{4+} + 4e \quad \text{(oxidation)} \\ C_6H_5N_2^+ + 4H^+ \rightarrow C_6H_5N_2H_4^+ - 4e \quad \text{(reduction)} \end{cases}$$

Method

Place one gram of aniline in a boiling-tube and add 5 ml of concentrated hydrochloric acid. Set the tube in a beaker of ice, and when the contents are cold add 1 gm of sodium nitrite dissolved in a little water. Prepare a solution by adding 6 g of anhydrous stannous chloride to 5 ml concentrated hydrochloric acid. Mix the two solutions and observe the formation of a white precipitate of phenyl-hydrazine hydrochloride ($C_6H_5 . N_2H_4^+Cl^-$). The reduction process is inefficient; some aniline hydrochloride will remain.

Oxidation Reactions in Organic Chemistry

8

Very powerful oxidation of organic compounds leads to a disruption of molecules with the production of a number of simple gaseous products. Carbon dioxide and water will always be formed. If sulphur or nitrogen is present, then sulphur dioxide or oxides of nitrogen will be formed. This complete oxidation occurs when materials burn in air. It is a process encouraged when heats of combustion are being measured. Normally this complete oxidation is avoided; reagents and conditions are selected so that some intermediate product is obtained.

Some common oxidations are given below. R represents an alkyl group.

(a) *Primary alcohols may be oxidized to aldehydes.

$$R.CH_2.OH - 2e \rightarrow R.CHO + 2H^+$$

e.g. ethyl alcohol $\rightarrow$ acetaldehyde

(b) Secondary alcohols may be oxidized to ketones.

$$\begin{array}{c} R \\ R \end{array}\!\!\!\!\!>CH.OH - 2e \rightarrow \begin{array}{c} R \\ R \end{array}\!\!\!\!\!>C=O + 2H^+$$

e.g. isopropyl alcohol $\rightarrow$ acetone

(c) Aldehydes may be oxidized to carboxylic acids.

$$R.CHO + H_2O - 2e \rightarrow R.COOH + 2H^+$$

e.g. acetaldehyde $\rightarrow$ acetic acid

(d) Carbon side chains on an aromatic nucleus may be oxidized to carboxylic acids or to aldehydes.

$$C_6H_5.CH_3 + 2H_2O - 6e \rightarrow C_6H_5COOH + 6H^+$$
toluene   benzoic acid

(e) Anodic oxidations.

e.g. acetate ions at an anode may produce carbon dioxide and ethane.

$$2CH_3 . COO^- - 2e \rightarrow C_2H_6 + 2CO_2$$

(f) Disproportionations.

Cuprous salts will often decompose to yield cupric salts and metallic copper.

$$2Cu^+ \rightarrow Cu^{++} + Cu$$

One cuprous ion is oxidized and the other is reduced. The process is called a *disproportionation*. Benzaldehyde in the presence of alkali undergoes this type of reaction, and the products are benzyl alcohol and benzoate ions.

$$C_6H_5 . CHO + H_2O - 2e \rightarrow C_6H_5COO^- + 3H^+ \quad \text{(oxidation)}$$
$$C_6H_5 . CHO + 2H^+ + 2e \rightarrow C_6H_5 . CH_2OH \qquad \text{(reduction)}$$

Overall

$$2C_6H_5 . CHO + H_2O \rightarrow C_6H_5 . COO^- + C_6H_5CH_2OH + H^+$$

Alkali removes the hydrogen ions formed.

Common oxidizing agents

(a) Nitric acid.

$$NO_3^- + 2H^+ + e \rightarrow NO_2 + H_2O$$

(b) Atmospheric oxygen.

$$O_2 + 4H^+ + 4e \rightarrow 2H_2O$$

(c) Potassium dichromate with acid.

$$Cr_2O_7^{--} + 14H^+ + 6e \rightarrow 2Cr^{3+} + 7H_2O$$

(d) Potassium permanganate with acid.

$$MnO_4^- + 8H^+ + 5e \rightarrow Mn^{++} + 4H_2O$$

(e) Hydrogen peroxide.

$$H_2O_2 + 2H^+ + 2e \rightarrow 2H_2O$$

Experiment 29. The oxidation of cane sugar to form oxalic acid

Concentrated nitric acid will oxidize cane sugar ($C_{12}H_{22}O_{11}$) producing oxalic acid $(COOH)_2$. The reaction is complex and is accompanied by the evolution of oxides of nitrogen. The experiment must be conducted in a fume cupboard.

Method

Place 25 g of sugar in a one-litre round-bottomed flask. Add 150 ml of concentrated nitric acid and heat the flask on a water-bath until the reaction becomes vigorous. Turn off the Bunsen burner, and allow the flask to remain in the water-bath until the reaction has subsided. Still working in a fume cupboard, transfer the contents of the flask into a large evaporating dish, and evaporate down to small bulk (20 ml). Allow the solution to cool, preferably on ice, and filter off the oxalic acid at a pump. The product may be recrystallized from hot water and then dried in a desiccator. Measure the yield.

(*a*) Test the product by placing a little in a test-tube, adding concentrated sulphuric acid, and then heating. Test the gases evolved by applying a lighted splint, secondly by passing them into lime water

$$(COOH)_2 - H_2O \rightarrow CO + CO_2$$

(*b*) Dissolve a few crystals in water, warm the solution and add a few drops of dilute H_2SO_4, then potassium permanganate solution. The permanganate is decolorized.

Experiment 30. To oxidize methyl alcohol to formaldehyde

$$2CH_3OH - 4e \rightarrow 2H.CHO + 4H^+$$
$$O_2 + 4H^+ + 4e \rightarrow 2H_2O$$

Addition: $2CH_3OH + O_2 \rightarrow 2H.CHO + 2H_2O$

Cover the bottom of a small beaker with methyl alcohol. Set a Bunsen burner under a tripod and gauze, and heat the gauze for a short time. Now remove the Bunsen and set the beaker on the hot gauze. When the alcohol is hot, introduce a hot platinum spiral, and hold the spiral immediately above the level of the alcohol using a pair of tongs (fig. 22). Identify formaldehyde by its smell, or test for it by holding a piece of filter paper, wet with ammoniacal silver nitrate, in the mouth of the beaker.

Ammoniacal silver nitrate is made by adding bench ammonia to silver nitrate solution to obtain a clear solution. The solution blackens on exposure to formaldehyde due to the formation of metallic silver.

$$2Ag^+ + 2e \rightarrow 2Ag \quad \text{(reduction)}$$

$$H.CHO + H_2O - 2e \rightarrow H.COO^- + 3H^+ \quad \text{(oxidation)}$$

Addition:

$$2Ag^+ + HCHO + H_2O \rightarrow 2Ag + H.COO^- + 3H^+$$

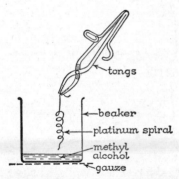

Fig. 22.—The catalytic oxidation of methyl alcohol

Experiment 31. The oxidation of ethyl alcohol to acetaldehyde or to acetic acid

Both these oxidations are carried out using a dichromate–acid system, and they illustrate how a change of conditions can change the products formed. The oxidations may be represented thus:

$$C_2H_5OH - 2e \rightarrow \underset{\text{acetaldehyde}}{CH_3CHO} + 2H^+$$

or $$C_2H_5OH + H_2O - 4e \rightarrow \underset{\text{acetic acid}}{CH_3.COOH} + 4H^+$$

Electrons are absorbed by the process:

$$Cr_2O_7^{--} + 14H^+ + 6e \rightarrow 2Cr^{3+} + 7H_2O$$

The equations show that the formation of the acid will be encouraged if a large amount of oxidizing agent is used. Similarly, if the reactions are regarded as occurring consecutively, the acid will be formed if acetaldehyde is retained in the reaction mixture. In practice, acetaldehyde is formed when sodium dichromate and alcohol are added to acid, and the product is allowed to escape immediately. Acetic acid is formed when alcohol is dropped into a mixture of dichromate–acid under reflux.

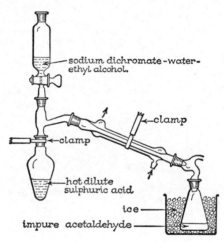

Fig. 23.—The preparation of acetaldehyde

The preparation of acetaldehyde

Set up the apparatus shown in fig. 23. Place 5 ml of water in the flask and add 2 ml of concentrated sulphuric acid slowly, agitating the flask continually. Put a piece of porous pot in the flask and then connect the flask to the still head.

Dissolve 5 g of sodium dichromate in 5 ml of water, add 4 ml of industrial spirit, and place the mixture in the dropping funnel. Pass a stream of water through the condenser and pack the receiver in crushed ice. Heat the dilute acid in the flask until it begins to boil, remove the flame, and allow the dichromate–alcohol to drop into the flask. The addition should take about 10 min. Impure acetaldehyde collects in the receiver, the main impurities being alcohol, water, and acetic acid.

Test the distillate

1. Place a little ammoniacal silver nitrate solution in a test-tube (p. 59). Add a few drops of distillate and warm the mixture. Acetaldehyde is a reducing agent.
2. Place a little Fehling's solution in a test-tube (p. 67), and add a few drops of distillate. Warm the mixture and observe the formation of cuprous oxide.
3. Add 1 ml of distillate to 1 ml of Schiff's reagent. Observe the purple coloration.
4. Do an iodoform test on the distillate. Use the method described in Experiment 73b.
5. Action of sodium hydroxide. Add a few millilitres of concentrated sodium hydroxide solution to a portion of the distillate. Warm the mixture and note the formation of a resin (see Experiment 40).
6. Aldehyde phenylhydrazone formation (see Experiment 37).

The preparation of acetic acid

Set up the apparatus as shown in fig. 24. One neck of the flask contains a condenser in the reflux position. A second neck contains a dropping funnel and the third is stoppered. Slowly add 3 ml of concentrated sulphuric acid to 5 ml of water, making sure that mixing is complete after each addition. Transfer the mixture to the flask. Weigh out 6 g of sodium dichromate and add this to the mixture in the flask. Put a piece of porous pot in the flask and connect the condenser, the funnel, and the stopper. Place a mixture of 1·5 ml of industrial spirit and 6 ml of water in the funnel. Pass water through the condenser, and drop the mixture into the flask slowly and with constant agitation. When addition is complete, heat the flask on a water-bath. Continue the heating for ten minutes.

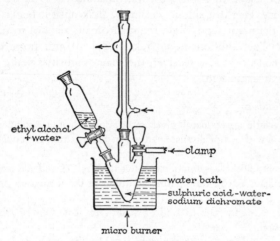

ethyl alcohol + water

clamp

water bath

sulphuric acid - water - sodium dichromate

micro burner

Fig. 24.—The preparation of acetic acid

Assemble the apparatus as shown in fig. 25. Perform a direct distillation using a micro burner, and collect 8 ml of distillate. The liquid collected contains some water and acetaldehyde, but the presence of acetic acid is indicated by the smell, and by applying the ferric chloride test.

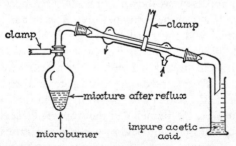

clamp

clamp

mixture after reflux

micro burner

impure acetic acid

Fig. 25.—Isolation

The ferric chloride test for acetate

The ferric chloride test must be worked using neutral solutions. Take a few drops of distillate, and add a little bench ammonia until the solution is alkaline to litmus paper. Boil the solution to expel excess ammonia (solution A). Prepare a neutral solution of ferric chloride by adding a few drops of bench sodium hydroxide to ferric chloride solution. Filter off the precipitate of ferric hydroxide and add the filtrate to solution A. The formation of a red coloration indicates acetate.

Additional test-tube reactions (Use stock acetic acid)

1. Add dilute acid to sodium carbonate solution. Observe the effervescence

$$CO_3^{--} + 2H^+ \rightarrow CO_2 + H_2O$$

2. *Ester formation.* Heat 1 ml of ethyl alcohol with a few drops of glacial acetic acid together with a few drops of concentrated sulphuric acid. Cool, and pour the products into water. Note the odour (Experiment 44).

Experiment 32. The oxidation of benzyl chloride to benzoic acid

Aromatic compounds, which have as a part of their structure a carbon chain connected directly to the benzene ring, are prone to oxidation. In such cases the side chain becomes converted to a carboxylic acid group. Some examples are given below.

$$C_6H_5 . CH_3 \rightarrow C_6H_5 . COOH$$
$$\text{toluene} \qquad \text{benzoic acid}$$

$$C_6H_4(CH_3)_2 \rightarrow C_6H_4 (COOH)_2$$
$$o. \text{xylene} \qquad \text{phthalic acid}$$

$$C_6H_5 . C_2H_5 \rightarrow C_6H_5 . COOH$$
$$\text{ethyl benzene} \qquad \text{benzoic acid}$$

$$C_6H_5 . CO . CH_3 \rightarrow C_6H_5 . COOH$$
$$\text{acetophenone} \qquad \text{benzoic acid}$$

Not all oxidizing agents bring about these changes equally well, and usually the simplest hydrocarbon side chain, i.e. —CH_3, is the hardest to oxidize. Because benzyl chloride is oxidized quickly, this is the substance used to illustrate the general method. The first stage in the reaction is the formation of benzyl alcohol.

$$C_6H_5CH_2Cl + OH^- \rightarrow C_6H_5CH_2OH + Cl^-$$
benzyl chloride   benzyl alcohol

Method

CAUTION: *Benzyl chloride is poisonous.*

Place 200 ml of water in a 500-ml round-bottomed flask. Dissolve 5 g of anhydrous sodium carbonate and 10 g of potassium permanganate in the water. Introduce 5 ml of benzyl chloride. Attach a reflux water condenser to the flask, and boil the mixture on a tripod and gauze until no oily drops of benzyl chloride remain. This stage might take $1\frac{1}{2}$ h (1). Allow the flask to cool, and transfer the contents to a large beaker. Precipitate benzoic acid by slowly adding concentrated hydrochloric acid with constant stirring until the solution is acid to litmus (2). Now add concentrated sodium sulphite solution dropwise with vigorous stirring. Continue the addition until all the manganese dioxide has reacted to form the soluble manganese dithionate (3). Cool the mixture and filter off the benzoic acid using a Büchner funnel. Wash the acid with cold water, and recrystallize it from hot water if it is required pure. Weigh the product and calculate the theoretical yield.

1 See p. 56

2 $$C_6H_5 . COO^- + H^+ \rightarrow C_6H_5 . COOH$$

3 $$SO_3^{--} + 2H^+ \rightarrow SO_2 + H_2O$$

$$2SO_2 + MnO_2 \rightarrow MnS_2O_6$$

Experiment 33. The preparation of ethane by anodic oxidation

When solutions of the salts of carboxylic acids are electrolysed, the anions move to the anode of the cell, and there lose electrons to the electrode. The products formed seem to depend upon the concentration of the solution and the nature of the anode. In the case of simple fatty acids, carbon dioxide is produced together with paraffin gases.

$$2CH_3 . COO^- - 2e \rightarrow C_2H_6 + 2CO_2$$

acetate ion   ethane

Carbon dioxide may be absorbed in alkali.

Method

Construct a cell as shown in fig. 26. Fill the inner and the outer compartments with a concentrated solution of sodium acetate placing a little ice in the anode compartment to reduce over-

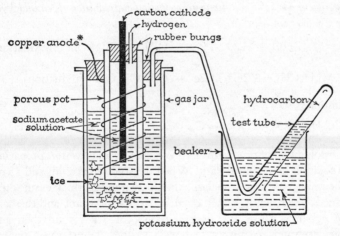

Fig. 26.—The anodic oxidation of sodium acetate

heating. Connect three 2-volt lead accumulators to form a 6-volt battery; connect the positive terminal to the copper electrode and the negative to the carbon electrode.

---

* The copper wire is sealed through the bung and is wrapped round the porous pot.

Collect the anode gases over dilute potassium hydroxide solution so that carbon dioxide is removed. Collect the cathode gas over water.

(i) Confirm that the cathode gas is hydrogen.
(ii) Ignite a tube of the anode gas.
(iii) Add a few drops of potassium permanganate to a tube of anode gas; shake the tube. Compare this with the reactions of ethylene and acetylene (Experiments 48, 51).

Use the same cell to electrolyse solutions of sodium succinate and sodium formate. Interpret the results.

Experiment 34. The simultaneous oxidation and reduction of benzaldehyde (the Cannizzaro reaction)

$$C_6H_5CHO + H_2O - 2e \rightarrow \underset{\text{benzoate ion}}{C_6H_5COO^-} + 3H^+ \text{ (oxidation)}$$

$$C_6H_5CHO + 2H^+ + 2e \rightarrow \underset{\text{benzyl alcohol}}{C_6H_5CH_2OH} \text{ (reduction)}$$

Addition:

$$2C_6H_5CHO + H_2O \rightarrow C_6H_5COO^- + C_6H_5CH_2OH + H^+$$

Dissolve 12 g of potassium hydroxide in 10 ml of water, preparing the solution in a conical flask. When the solution is cold, add 15 ml of benzaldehyde, cork the flask, and shake it until a thick emulsion is formed. The reaction which occurs is very exothermic and the flask will get hot. Allow the flask to stand for a day, and then add sufficient water to dissolve all solid matter. Transfer the benzyl alcohol suspension to a separating funnel, and ether-extract to remove the benzyl alcohol. Obtain the alcohol from the ether by the method described on p. 32.

CAUTION: *Avoid all naked flames when using ether.*

Pour the aqueous solution of potassium benzoate into a beaker. Slowly and with constant stirring, add concentrated hydrochloric acid until the mixture is acid. When the contents of the beaker are cold, filter off the benzoic acid at a pump. Wash the product with cold water and then dry it in a desiccator. Compare the weights of benzoic acid and benzyl alcohol obtained with those calculated from the equation.

Experiment 35. An oxidation by hydrogen peroxide (Fenton's reagent)

Prepare a dilute solution of tartaric acid, $C_2H_2(OH)_2(COOH)_2$. To this add a drop of ferrous sulphate solution followed by a few drops of hydrogen peroxide. Make the solution alkaline with bench sodium hydroxide and note the production of a violet coloration.

The violet coloration is due to the formation of ferric dihydroxy maleic acid. Ferric ions are produced by oxidation of the ferrous salt.

$$Fe^{++} - e \rightarrow Fe^{3+}$$

Dihydroxy maleic acid by the oxidation of tartaric acid.

$$C_2H_2(OH)_2(COOH)_2 - 2e \rightarrow C_2(OH)_2(COOH)_2 + 2H^+$$

During the process, hydrogen peroxide is reduced.

$$H_2O_2 + 2H^+ + 2e \rightarrow 2H_2O$$

Experiment 36. The oxidation of acetaldehyde by cupric ions (Fehling's test). The preparation of Fehling's solution

Solution A: Dissolve 17 g of copper sulphate pentahydrate in 250 ml of water.

Solution B: Dissolve 86 g of sodium potassium tartrate (Rochelle salt) in warm water. Prepare another solution of 30 g of sodium hydroxide. Cool the two solutions, mix them, and make up to 250 ml with water.

Mix equal volumes of A and B to make up the Fehling's solution required for immediate use ($\frac{1}{3}$ test-tube). Solutions A and B should be stored separately for future use because the mixed solution deteriorates.

Method

Add a few drops of acetaldehyde to Fehling's solution. Slowly bring the mixture to the boil, and observe the formation of a solid which varies in colour from green to red. Repeat the experiment using glucose, and again using cane sugar. With glucose there is the production of fairly pure cuprous oxide.

$$2Cu^{++} + 2e \rightarrow 2Cu^+ \quad \text{(reduction)}$$
$$2Cu^+ + 2OH^- \rightarrow Cu_2O + H_2O$$

9

Valency (The study of forces between atoms)

Any theory of valency must be an answer to a number of questions which arise from observations on the behaviour of materials.

1. Why do interatomic forces differ so widely in their magnitude?
2. Why do some forces give rise to molecules having definite shape?
3. Why do the forces result in molecules containing a definite number of atoms?

The significance of these questions is developed if they are related to the chemistry of water.

1. About 500 calories of heat are required to convert one gram of water to steam, at the boiling point of the liquid. This is a measure of the work necessary to overcome the attraction of water molecules upon each other (ignoring the fact that some heat is used in doing work on the atmosphere). One gram–molecule of water (18 g) will require 9000 calories.

(i) $\quad H_2O \text{(liquid)} \rightarrow H_2O \text{(gas)}; \quad \Delta H = +9000 \text{ cal}$

The heat required to atomize water is of a different order.

(ii) $\quad H_2O \text{(gas)} \rightarrow 2H + O; \quad \Delta H = +100,000 \text{ cal}$

The forces between atoms within the molecule are much greater than those between neighbouring molecules.

2. There is strong evidence that a water molecule is not linear, but that lines joining the centres of the hydrogen atoms with that of the oxygen intersect, forming an angle of about 104°. Similarly the molecules of methane and ammonia have definite shape (fig. 27).

69

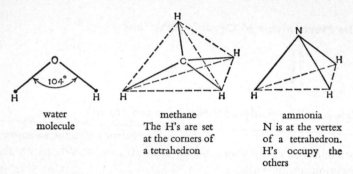

water
molecule

methane
The H's are set
at the corners of
a tetrahedron

ammonia
N is at the vertex
of a tetrahedron.
H's occupy the
others

Fig. 27.—The shape of molecules

3. The oxygen atom is able to bind two hydrogen atoms. H_2O is a very stable combination. Why are the combinations HO, H_3O, H_4O, etc., not nearly so stable?

The electronic theory of valency

The questions presented are answered by considering the structures of individual atoms. These consist of a small positively charged centre or nucleus, and this is screened by units of negative electricity (electrons) which are situated at a great distance from the nucleus.

Forces of the magnitude described in equation (ii) are due to atoms sharing electrons. If an atom A and an atom B share one electron, then they are bound by a *single electron bond*. The shared electron exerts an attractive force on both nuclei, and if it is located between the two, then it will bind them together. A shared pair of electrons is a common bond, and this is represented by a line joining the two atoms. If $\overset{\times}{\times}$ represents a pair of electrons which are shared by A and B to form a molecule AB, this may be represented as shown in (a) below. Often, chemical bonding is the result of sharing two pairs of electrons. This linkage is represented by a double line between the atoms as shown in (b) below.

(a) $\qquad$ A $\overset{\times}{\times}$ B $\quad$ or $\quad$ A—B

(b) $\qquad$ A $\overset{\times}{\underset{\times}{\times}}$ B $\quad$ or $\quad$ A=B

(c) The structure of ethylene, C_2H_4

$$H \overset{\times\,\times}{} \quad \overset{\times}{\underset{\times}{}} \quad \overset{\times}{} H$$

H×× ×× ×× H
    C × C
H ×× ×× ×× H   or   the structure with C=C double bond, H and H on each carbon

The electrons forming a 'pair' bond may be provided, one from each atom, and in this case the bonding is said to be *covalent* (see (a) below). Sometimes both electrons are provided by one atom, and in this case the bond is said to be *co-ionic* or *dative*. This type of bonding is represented by an arrow which indicates the origin of the electrons (see (b) below).

(a) $\qquad$ A× + B× $\quad$ combine to give $\quad$ A $\overset{\times}{\times}$ B $\quad$ (A—B)

(b) $\qquad$ A $\overset{\times}{\times}$ + B $\quad$ combine to give $\quad$ A $\overset{\times}{\times}$ B $\quad$ (A→B)

An equal sharing of an electron pair between A and B is unusual; it will only occur when they are identical atoms. In H_2, Cl_2, O_2, N_2, both atoms exert the same influence on the electron pairs because the nuclear charges on the bound atoms are identical. In other cases, the atom having the greater attraction for electrons will claim more than an equal share of the bonding electrons. Unequal sharing results in a bond in which the terminal atoms have unequal electrical potentials, and the bond is said to be *semipolar*. This may be represented thus:

$$A \overset{\times}{\times} B \quad \text{or} \quad \overset{\delta-\quad\delta+}{A—B}$$

Sometimes a remote atom may influence the polar nature of the bond, and this phenomenon is called the *inductive effect*. So it is that monochloracetic acid is a stronger acid than acetic acid. In the former the chlorine atom attracts electrons strongly, and the remote proton is liberated more easily. Arrows indicate the displacement of electrons.

$$\overset{\delta-}{Cl}\underset{\longleftarrow}{\overset{\overset{\displaystyle H}{\underset{\displaystyle |}{\longleftarrow}}}{\underset{\overset{\displaystyle |}{\displaystyle H}}{C}}}\underset{\longleftarrow}{C}\overset{\nearrow\quad O}{\underset{\nwarrow}{}}\overset{}{\underset{O\underset{\longleftarrow}{-}H}{}}\overset{\delta+}{}$$

When sharing is very unequal, it is useful to consider the electron pair as belonging to one of the atoms, the bonding forces being electrostatic in character. In these cases the bonding is said to be *electrovalent* or *ionic*.

$$A\times\ +\ B\times\qquad gives\qquad \overset{-}{A}\ \overset{\times}{\underset{\times}{}}\ \overset{+}{B}$$

Localized and delocalized electrons

The properties of a large number of compounds are satisfactorily explained in terms of the types of bonding referred to. The essential character of these is that the electron pairs are *localized*; they exert an intense influence between two atoms. Sometimes, however, we have to suppose that a pair of electrons is *delocalized*. The behaviour of the molecule cannot be explained by assigning a fixed location to the electrons; they are regarded as belonging to the molecule as a whole. Benzene is a case in point. It has the molecular formula C_6H_6 and, ignoring delocalization, the structure may be represented as shown in (*a*) opposite. This is wrong in view of the following facts.

1. X-ray analysis shows that in the benzene molecule all carbon–carbon bonds are the same length. The same technique applied to aliphatic compounds shows that the C=C bond is not the same length as the C—C bond.

2. The measured heat of combustion of benzene differs from that obtained by calculating it on the basis of the structure given.

3. The ethylene molecule has a double bond $\left(\overset{H}{\underset{H}{>}}C=C\overset{H}{\underset{H}{<}}\right)$ and if benzene also contains this type of carbon–carbon linkage, then the two should have similar chemical properties. This is not the case.

Benzene behaves as though its molecule contains three pairs of delocalized electrons, and this is represented in (*b*) below.

The shape of molecules

Directional valency may be explained by using the idea that an electron pair will repel other pairs. This mutual repulsion will occur whether the electron pairs constitute chemical bonds or not. In water, methane, and ammonia, the O, C, and N have the same electronic structures. They each contain four pairs of electrons. These pairs will distribute themselves for maximum separation as is shown in the table below. Small differences in bond angle may be due to the differing repulsions of terminal nuclei.

TABLE I

Compound	Plane representation of the molecule	3-dimensional	Bond angle
H_2O			104·5°
NH_3			106°
CH_4			108°

Experimental insight into mechanism (The rate laws)

The rate of the reaction

$$A + CD \rightarrow AC + D$$

may be taken as the change in the amount of product D with time. The value of dD/dt may be measured experimentally at any instant, and studies show that it is influenced by a number of factors. Temperature, the presence of impurities in A or CD, the concentrations of the reactants, may all have influence. Each of these factors may be the subject of individual studies, and the method of work is to keep all other factors constant whilst examining one. To study the influence of the concentrations of the reactants upon the rate, dD/dt is measured at a number of reactant concentrations, the temperature remaining constant. If [CD] and [A] represent the concentrations of these substances, experiment may reveal the relationships (rate laws)

(a)
$$\frac{dD}{dt} = K[CD] \quad \text{first order}$$

or

(b)
$$\frac{dD}{dt} = K_1[A][CD] \quad \text{second order}$$

It might be that the *rate law* is more complicated than either of these —only experiment will tell. K and K_1 are called *velocity constants*, and are functions of the temperature.

If a rate law includes one concentration term only, then the reaction is said to be *first order*. (a) is a case of this kind, the concentration of A having no influence on the rate of reaction. (b) shows that two concentration terms are required to express the rate; in this case the reaction is said to be *second order*. Any mechanism which is proposed for the reaction must be consistent with the experimentally determined order.

Reaction. First order. Suggested mechanism

Suppose that the reaction takes place in two stages: the first, the dissociation of CD, the second an association of A with C. Suppose, too, that the dissociation is slow and the association fast.

1. $$CD \rightarrow C + D \quad \text{(slow)}$$
2. $$A + C \rightarrow CA \quad \text{(fast)}$$

The measured rate of reaction (dD/dt) must be the rate of the slow reaction 1, and this is independent of the concentration of A.

Reaction. Second order. Suggested mechanism

1. $$A + CD \rightarrow ACD \quad \text{(an intermediate compound—slow)}$$
2. $$ACD \rightarrow AC + D \quad \text{(fast)}$$

Here the overall rate will be determined by the rate of formation of the intermediate. In this case both [A] and [CD] will influence the rate.

In the formation of the intermediate, A approaches CD in the line of the molecule, and as it does so D recedes from C. At some stage the intermediate compound is formed:

$$A \rightarrow \qquad\qquad C—D$$
$$A \rightarrow \qquad C—D$$
$$A—C———D \quad \text{[intermediate]}$$
$$A—C \qquad D \rightarrow$$

During the course of this reaction, the energy of the A/C/D system changes, and this may be represented graphically (fig. 28 on p. 76). At X, A and CD are far apart and the energy of the system is low. At Y, the intermediate compound exists and the system has maximum energy. Portion YZ relates to the recession of D. Energy is required to convert the reactants to the intermediate form, and this is called the *energy of activation*.

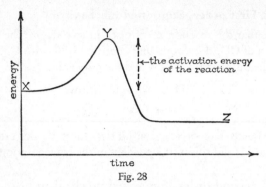

Fig. 28

Steric factors

It is often necessary to consider the shape and size of molecules undergoing chemical reactions. Often reactions fail to occur, or result in unexpected products, because part of a molecule presents an obstruction. The bromine atoms in CH_3Br; $CH_3 . CH_2 . Br$; $(CH_3)_2CH . Br$; $(CH_3)_3C . Br$ may be replaced by hydroxyl groups (OH), to form alcohols, but it is progressively more difficult to do this. This may be explained by supposing that the methyl groups hinder the formation of an intermediate, $OH \ldots (CH_3)_3C \ldots Br$.

Electrophiles and nucleophiles

Chemical reagents may be divided into two classes. There are those which will donate electrons readily, and those which readily accept them. When an acid reacts with a base, then the process is one of interaction between these two types of reagent.

$$HCl + NaOH \rightarrow NaCl + H_2O$$

ionically $\quad H^+ + OH^- \rightarrow H_2O$

The hydrogen ion readily accepts electrons; it is said to be *electrophilic*. The hydroxyl ion donates electrons and is said to be *nucleophilic*. When the two reagents fulfil their potential, then a chemical bond results.

In the illustration given, there is no problem in deciding which reagent is electrophilic and which is nucleophilic. The charge on a hydrogen ion will attract electrons, and these will form the helium structure about the nucleus. Similarly, the charge on a hydroxyl ion will repel electrons, and the electrons about the oxygen atom which are not involved in chemical bonds may be donated (Table II).

TABLE II

ELECTROPHILES		NUCLEOPHILES	
Formula	Electron structure★	Formula	Electron structure★
H^+			
Br^+	$\left[\times \overset{\times \times}{\underset{\times \times}{Br}} \times \right]^+$	$[OH]^-$	$\left[\overset{\times \times}{\underset{\times \times}{\times O}} \times H \right]^-$
NO_2^+	$\left[\overset{\times \ \ \times}{\underset{\times \ \ \times}{O}} \overset{\times \ \ \times}{\underset{\times \ \ \times}{N}} \overset{\times \ \ \times}{\underset{\times \ \ \times}{O}} \right]^+$	Br^-	$\left[\times \overset{\times \times}{\underset{\times \times}{Br}} \times \right]^-$
AlCl$_3$	$\left[\overset{\times \times}{\underset{\times \times}{\times Cl \times}} \overset{\times \times}{\underset{\times \times}{\times Cl \times Al}} \overset{\times \times}{\underset{\times \times}{\times Cl \times}} \right]$	$[NH_2]^-$	$\left[\overset{H}{\underset{\times \times}{\times N \times H}} \right]^-$
		NH$_3$	$\overset{H}{\underset{H}{\times N \times H}}$
BF$_3$	$\left[\overset{\times \times}{\underset{\times \times}{\times F \times}} \overset{\times \times}{\underset{\times \times}{\times F \times B}} \overset{\times \times}{\underset{\times \times}{\times F \times}} \right]$	H_2O	$\left[\overset{H}{\underset{\times \times}{\times O \times H}} \right]$

Nucleophiles.—Anions, or molecules containing electron pairs which are not involved in bonding, and which donate electrons during reaction.

Electrophiles.—Cations, or molecules, which during the course of reaction accept electrons. The electrons accepted enter an incomplete shell.

★ The electronic structures show the outer shells only, inner complete shells are not represented.

Sometimes the nature of a reagent is not nearly so obvious. In the reaction of ammonia with an acid, the ammonium ion is formed.

$$NH_3 + H^+ \rightarrow NH_4^+$$

The hydrogen ion is electrophilic, receiving electrons, whilst the ammonia molecule donates electrons. Table II shows the structure of the ammonia molecule.

Condensation Reactions

10

When organic molecules combine with the elimination of a small molecule, then the reaction is called a *condensation*. The main product, often of large molecular weight, is called a *condensation product*. The reacting molecules may be identical or dissimilar, and any number of them may be involved in the process.

An alcohol (R.OH) may combine with a carboxylic acid (R^1.COOH) to form a condensation product,

$$R.OH + HOOC.R^1 \rightarrow R.O.OC.R^1 + H_2O$$

A similar condensation between an alcohol (HO.R^2.OH) and an acid (HOOC.R^3.COOH) may lead to the formation of a large molecule,

$$nHO.R^2.OH + nHOOC.R^3.COOH$$
$$\rightarrow HO.R^2.O.(OC.R^3.CO.OR^2.O)_{n-1}OC.R^3.COOH$$
$$+ (n-1)H_2O$$

The mechanism of condensation reactions

Many condensation reactions involve molecules containing a carbonyl group $\left(\diagup\!\!\!\diagdown C{=}O \right)$. Aldehydes (R.CHO), ketones (R$_2$CO), carboxylic acids, and their derivatives all include this linkage in their structures. Molecules condensing with carbonyl compounds have a common feature—they are nucleophilic in character (page 76). Condensation reactions work via an intermediate addition product; this then undergoes a rearrangement with the elimination of a small molecule. The reactivity of the carbonyl group may be explained by supposing that a pair of electrons forming

79

one of the carbon–oxygen bonds may be located at the oxygen atom. Such a system is written $\overset{+}{>}C—\overset{-}{O}$, where the carbon atom is positively charged and the oxygen negatively. The carbon atom will attract any nucleophilic group, and we might expect a chemical linkage to form here.

The formation of oximes (see Experiment 38)

Hydroxylamine has a structure in which the nitrogen atom includes a lone pair of electrons ($\overset{x}{x}$). These may be donated to the carbon atom of a carbonyl linkage. When this happens the positive charge is transferred from the carbon atom.

Addition $\quad >\overset{+}{C}—\overset{-}{O} + \overset{x}{x}NH_2OH \rightarrow \left[>C\overset{O^-}{\underset{NH_2OH^+}{\overset{x}{x}}} \right]$

Elimination $\quad >C\overset{O^-}{\underset{NH_2OH^+}{<}} \rightarrow >C\overset{}{\underset{N—OH}{\diagdown}} + H_2O$

The formation of phenylhydrazones (see Experiment 37)

Phenylhydrazine is nucleophilic because of a lone pair of electrons on the terminal nitrogen atom.

Addition $\quad >C^+—O^- + \overset{x}{x}NH_2.NH.C_6H_5 \rightarrow \left[>C\overset{O^-}{\underset{NH_2.NH.C_6H_5^+}{\overset{x}{x}}} \right]$

Elimination $\quad >C\overset{O^-}{\underset{NH_2.NH.C_6H_5^+}{<}} \rightarrow >C\overset{O^-}{\underset{N.NH.C_6H_5}{<}} + H_2O$

$\qquad\qquad\qquad\qquad\qquad\qquad\qquad\qquad$ phenylhydrazone

The condensation of aldehydes in the presence of alkalis (see Experiment 40.

Hydroxyl ions bring about the formation of a nucleophilic group ($\bar{C}H_2 . CHO$) by removing a proton from the acetaldehyde molecule $CH_3 . CHO$. The nucleophile then reacts as follows,

Addition $\quad \begin{matrix} CH_3 \\ \diagdown \\ H \diagup \end{matrix} \overset{+}{C} - \bar{O} + \bar{C}H_2 . C \diagup^{O}_{\diagdown H} \rightarrow \left[\begin{matrix} CH_3 \\ \diagdown \\ H \diagup \end{matrix} C \diagup^{O^-}_{\diagdown CH_2 - C \diagup^{O}_{\diagdown H}} \right]$

Elimination $\quad \begin{matrix} CH_3 \\ \diagdown \\ H \diagup \end{matrix} C \diagup^{O^-}_{\diagdown CH_2 - C \diagup^{O}_{\diagdown H}} \rightarrow \begin{matrix} CH_3 \\ \diagdown \\ H \diagup \end{matrix} C = CH - CHO + OH^-$

Esterification (see Experiment 44)

In the reaction of acetic acid with ethyl alcohol, molecules of the former contain a carbonyl group; the oxygen atom of an ethyl alcohol molecule contains lone pairs of electrons. Sulphuric acid acts as a catalyst by providing hydrogen ions.

Addition $\quad CH_3 - \overset{\displaystyle O^-}{\underset{\displaystyle OH}{\overset{|}{\underset{|}{C^+}}}} + \overset{\times \times}{\underset{\times \times}{O}} \diagup^{C_2H_5}_{\diagdown H} + H^+ \rightarrow \left[CH_3 - \overset{\displaystyle OH}{\underset{\displaystyle OH}{\overset{|}{\underset{|}{C}}}} - \overset{+}{O} \diagup^{C_2H_5}_{\diagdown H} \right]$

$\qquad\qquad\qquad$ acetic acid

Elimination $\quad CH_3 - \overset{\displaystyle OH}{\underset{\displaystyle OH}{\overset{|}{\underset{|}{C}}}} - \overset{+}{O} \diagup^{C_2H_5}_{\diagdown H} \rightarrow CH_3 - \underset{\displaystyle \underset{O}{\parallel}}{C} - O - C_2H_5 + H_2O + H^+$

$\qquad\qquad\qquad\qquad\qquad\qquad$ ethyl acetate

Experiment 37. The preparation of benzaldehyde phenylhydrazone

Aldehydes and ketones undergo condensation with phenylhydrazine, and produce compounds called *hydrazones*. For aldehydes and ketones of low molecular weight, these products are difficult to crystallize, and for this reason benzaldehyde is used to illustrate the reaction. The carbonyl compounds are easily regained from combination, by hydrolysis, and hydrazones of high molecular weight are easy to purify and have sharp melting points. For these reasons, hydrazones are often prepared for the identification of aldehydes and ketones of high molecular weight.

$$C_6H_5 . CHO + NH_2 . NH . C_6H_5 \rightarrow C_6H_5 . CH{=}N . NH . C_6H_5$$
benzaldehyde   phenylhydrazine   benzaldehyde phenylhydrazone
$$+ H_2O$$

Method

Make a solution of phenylhydrazine acetate by pouring a few drops of phenylhydrazine into a test-tube and adding an equal volume of glacial acetic acid. *CARE.* PHENYLHYDRAZINE SHOULD NOT COME INTO CONTACT WITH THE SKIN. Dilute the solution with two volumes of water. Add the solution to a few drops of benzaldehyde in a test-tube. Observe the precipitation of benzaldehyde phenylhydrazone.

Repeat the experiment using a solution of 2:4 dinitro phenylhydrazine in glacial acetic acid. This forms a hydrazone having a higher melting point, and which is easier to crystallize.

Experiment 38. The preparation of acetoxime

With hydroxylamine, aldehydes and ketones undergo condensations to form oximes. With acetone,

$$(CH_3)_2C{=}O + H_2N . OH \rightarrow (CH_3)_2C{=}N . OH + H_2O$$
acetoxime

Mix 5 g of hydroxylamine hydrochloride and 10 ml of water in a boiling-tube. Add a solution of 3 g of sodium hydroxide in 10 ml of water. Cool the mixture in a beaker of ice. Add 7 ml of acetone and stir well. Observe the slow formation of acetoxime crystals over a period of several hours.

Experiment 39. The condensation of formaldehyde and ammonia

$$6CH_2O + 4NH_3 \rightarrow (CH_2)_6N_4 + 6H_2O$$
hexamethylene
tetramine

Place 5 ml of formaldehyde solution in an evaporating dish and slowly add 5 ml of 0·88 ammonia solution. Stir the mixture for a few minutes and then evaporate it slowly on a water-bath. Observe the formation of crystals of hexamethylene tetramine.

Experiment 40. The condensation of acetaldehyde in the presence of alkalis

Warm 1 ml of acetaldehyde with a few millilitres of concentrated sodium hydroxide solution. Observe the formation of a yellow-red resin.

1. Addition ... $+ CH_3CHO + CH_3 CHO + CH_3CHO + ... \rightarrow$

$$...-CH_2-CH-CH_2-CH-CH_2-CH-...$$
$$\quad\quad\quad\quad | \quad\quad\quad\quad | \quad\quad\quad\quad |$$
$$\quad\quad\quad OH \quad\quad\quad OH \quad\quad\quad OH$$

2. Elimination $-CH=CH-CH=CH-CH=CH- + 3H_2O$
resin

Experiment 41. Some condensations of phenyldiazonium chloride

The condensation of diazonium compounds with other aromatic substances is used in the preparation of dyes. The mechanism of condensation differs from that described earlier because the phenyl-diazonium ion is electrophilic. Phenyldiazonium chloride has the structure $(C_6H_5.N_2^+).Cl^-$, and the cation will link at some point in another molecule where electrons may be provided (see p. 115). When aniline reacts with acid, the change may be represented by

$$C_6H_5NH_2 + H^+ \rightarrow C_6H_5NH_3^+$$

In the presence of nitrous acid ($NaNO_2 + HCl$) a chemical reaction occurs.

$$C_6H_5NH_3^+ + HNO_2 \rightarrow C_6H_5N_2^+ \quad + 2H_2O$$
phenyldiazonium ion

Phenyldiazonium chloride will condense with

(a) phenol

$$C_6H_5N_2{}^+Cl^- + C_6H_5OH \rightarrow C_6H_5N_2C_6H_4OH + H^+Cl^-$$

(b) β naphthol

$$C_6H_5N_2{}^+Cl^- + C_{10}H_7.OH \rightarrow C_6H_5N_2.C_{10}H_6.OH + H^+Cl^-$$

(c) dimethylaniline

$$C_6H_5N_2{}^+Cl^- + C_6H_5.N(CH_3)_2 \rightarrow C_6H_5.N_2.C_6H_4.N(CH_3)_2 + H^+Cl^-$$

Method

Dissolve a few drops of aniline in dilute hydrochloric acid, cool the solution in a beaker of ice. Prepare a solution of sodium nitrite in water and, after cooling it, pour it into the cold acid solution. Keep the diazonium solution on ice.

Prepare in three separate tubes, solutions of phenol in sodium hydroxide solution; β naphthol in sodium hydroxide solution; dimethylaniline in dilute hydrochloric acid. Add a few drops of the diazonium solution to each of the three tubes and observe the coloured condensation products formed.

Experiment 42. The preparation of phenolphthalein

Phthalic anhydride and phenol may condense to form phenolphthalein.

$$C_6H_4.C_2O_3 + 2C_6H_5.OH \rightarrow C_6H_4.C_2O_2.(C_6H_4.OH)_2 + H_2O$$

Place a few crystals of phthalic anhydride in a test-tube, add a little phenol, and then a few drops of concentrated sulphuric acid. Warm the mixture gently for a minute and then allow the mixture to cool. Transfer a drop of the product to a beaker containing sodium hydroxide solution. Note the purple colour characteristic of phenolphthalein in alkaline solution.

Experiment 43. The condensation of urea to form biuret

$$2NH_2.CO.NH_2 \rightarrow \underset{\text{biuret}}{NH_2.CO.NH.CO.NH_2} + NH_3$$

Place a little urea in a test-tube, warm it gently just above its melting point. Observe the evolution of ammonia, and the formation of solid biuret. Dissolve the solid in dilute sodium hydroxide solution, cool the mixture, and add one drop of copper sulphate solution. Note the formation of a pink coloration. (The biuret test.)

Experiment 44. The preparation of ethyl acetate

Ethyl acetate belongs to the class of compounds called the *esters*. These are produced by the condensation of alcohols with carboxylic acids, and the process is termed *esterification*. When ethyl alcohol and acetic acid are mixed at a particular temperature, then an equilibrium is established.

$$CH_3 . COOH + C_2H_5 . OH \rightleftharpoons CH_3 . COOC_2H_5 + H_2O$$
$$\text{ethyl acetate}$$

The equilibrium is disturbed to give high yields of the ester by carrying out the reaction in the presence of concentrated sulphuric acid.

Ethyl acetate may also be prepared by the acetylation of ethyl alcohol using acetyl chloride $(CH_3 . CO . Cl)$ or acetic anhydride $((CH_3CO)_2O)$. In the first case hydrogen chloride is eliminated; in the second, water. These reactions are called *acetylations* because the acetyl group (CH_3CO) is introduced into a molecule.

$$C_2H_5 . OH + CH_3 . CO . Cl \rightarrow CH_3 . CO . OC_2H_5 + HCl$$
$$C_2H_5 . OH + (CH_3 . CO)_2O \rightarrow CH_3 . CO . OC_2H_5 + CH_3 . COOH$$

Method

Set up the apparatus shown in fig. 29 (p. 86).

Place 2 ml of ethyl alcohol in the flask and slowly introduce 2 ml of concentrated sulphuric acid, swirling the flask after each addition. Now mix 7 ml of alcohol and 7 ml of glacial acetic acid, and place the mixture in the separating funnel. Connect the flask and heat it with a low flame until the mixture becomes very dark. Start the addition of the mixture in the funnel and adjust the addition so that it is at the same rate as the distillation. When all the mixture has been added, transfer the distillate to a separating funnel. Likely impurities in the product are alcohol, acetic acid, and sulphur dioxide. Add 5 ml of concentrated sodium carbonate solution and cautiously shake the funnel, releasing the pressure at frequent intervals. (Acetic acid and sulphurous acid react with the soda to form carbon dioxide.) Allow two layers to form and discard the lower layer. Make a

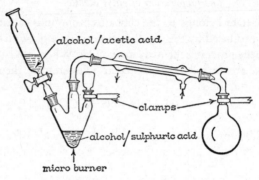

Fig. 29.—The preparation of ethyl acetate

solution of 5 g of calcium chloride in 5 ml of water and add this to the impure ethyl acetate. Shake the funnel so that the unconverted alcohol becomes dissolved in the aqueous layer. Discard the lower layer. Dry the product by placing it in contact with anhydrous calcium chloride in a stoppered tube. After $\frac{1}{2}$ h decant the ester into a distilling flask. Use a water-bath to distil the product, collecting the fraction boiling at 74–79°C (fig. 4). Measure the yield and compare it with the theoretical value obtained from the equation.

Experiment 45. The acetylation of ethyl alcohol (2)

To 1 ml of ethyl alcohol in a test-tube add 1 ml of acetyl chloride. CAUTION. *Acetyl chloride vapour is toxic. The reaction must be done in a fume cupboard. Wear rubber gloves.* Addition must be very slow and the test-tube cooled under a tap. Add 1 ml of brine and observe the layer of ethyl acetate forming at the surface. Recognize the product by its smell.

Experiment 46. The acetylation of aniline to form acetanilide

Place 5 ml of aniline in a pear-shaped flask and introduce 8 ml of acetic anhydride, slowly and with shaking. Connect an air condenser (fig. 30). Reflux the mixture for 15 min using a micro burner. Pour a few drops of the mixture into a beaker of water and observe

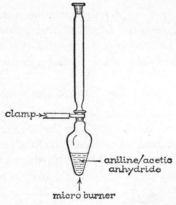

clamp→

— aniline/acetic anhydride

↑ micro burner

Fig. 30.—The acetylation of aniline

the precipitation of acetanilide. If the test is negative, continue the reflux; if it is positive, pour all the product into cold water. Filter the acetanilide using suction, and wash the product with cold water. Recrystallize the solid from hot water, dry it in a desiccator, and determine its melting point (114°C). Measure the yield and compare it with the theoretical value.

$$C_6H_5.NH_2 + (CH_3.CO)_2O \rightarrow C_6H_5.NH.CO.CH_3 + CH_3.COOH$$

Polymerization Reactions

11

A polymerization is the union of two or more identical molecules to form a larger, there being no other product formed. The polymer, as the product is called, has the same empirical formula as the monomer (reacting molecule).

Experiment 47. The conversion of acetaldehyde to paraldehyde

Add one drop of concentrated sulphuric acid to a few millilitres of acetaldehyde in a test-tube. Shake the tube and, if the reaction shows signs of becoming violent, cool the tube under the tap. When the reaction has subsided, add water to the product and note its insolubility. During the reaction paraldehyde is formed.

$$3CH_3 . CHO \rightarrow C_6H_{12}O_3$$

Paraldehyde has the constitution

Experiment 48. To prepare acetylene and polymerize this to benzene

Set up the apparatus shown in fig. 31, and place a mixture of sand and calcium carbide in the flask. Drop water into the flask so that a steady production of gas is obtained (1). Collect a few jars of acetylene by displacement of water, and test them in the following way.

(*a*) Ignite a jar and note the smoky flame. This is characteristic of compounds having a high proportion of carbon in their constitution.

(*b*) Add a few millilitres of potassium permanganate solution made alkaline with a little sodium hydroxide solution. Shake the jar and observe any colour change.

(*c*) Add a few millilitres of bromine water and shake the jar. Observe the slow decolorization of the bromine water (2).

(*d*) Make a solution of ammoniacal silver nitrate (p. 59) and pour it into a jar of the gas. Observe the formation of solid silver acetylide (3).

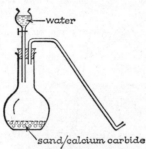

Fig. 31.—The preparation of acetylene

(1)	$CaC_2 + 2H_2O \rightarrow Ca(OH)_2 + C_2H_2$ (acetylene)
ionically	$C_2^{--} + 2H_2O \rightarrow 2OH^- + C_2H_2$
(2)	$C_2H_2 + Br_2 \rightarrow C_2H_2Br_2$
(3)	$C_2H_2 + 2AgNO_3 \rightarrow C_2Ag_2 + 2HNO_3$
ionically	$C_2H_2 + 2Ag^+ \rightarrow C_2Ag_2 + 2H^+$

(*e*) *Polymerization* (work in a fume cupboard). Prepare the apparatus shown in fig. 32. Seal one end of a piece of wide-bore hard-glass tubing in a Bunsen flame. Next bend it as shown, so that the bend is about 6 in from the closed end. Fill the tube with mercury using a tray to collect any metal which spills over. Invert the tube in a dish of mercury and then clamp it securely.

Prepare acetylene, using the method described, but this time bubble the gas through a solution of copper sulphate contained in a wash bottle (removal of phosphine). Collect the gas over the mercury until the level has fallen to 6 in above the level in the dish. Mark the position of the mercury level by sticking a small piece of paper on the tube. Wrap copper gauze round the sealed end as shown, and then heat the gauze to dull redness for twenty minutes. Make sure that gas does not escape on expanding. Allow the tube to cool and observe the final level of the mercury. Observe the droplets of 'oil' on the inside of the tube.

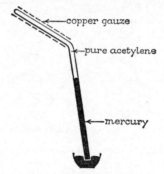

Fig. 32.—The polymerization of acetylene

$$3C_2H_2 \rightarrow C_6H_6 \quad (\text{benzene})$$

Addition Reactions

12

When two molecules join together to form a third, and no other molecule is produced, then the reaction is called an *addition*. Molecules which undergo addition are said to be *unsaturated*, and the property is associated with certain linkages within the molecules. The carbonyl group $\diagup C = O$, which is common to aldehydes and ketones, may lead to addition with molecules of type HX.

$$\diagup C = O + HX \rightarrow \diagup C \diagdown \begin{smallmatrix} OH \\ X \end{smallmatrix} \quad \text{(addition product)}$$

Carbon/carbon double bonds or triple bonds often lead to addition with compounds of type XY.

$$\diagup C = C \diagdown + XY \rightarrow \diagup \underset{X}{C} - \underset{Y}{C} \diagdown$$

or

$$-C \equiv C- + XY \rightarrow -\underset{X}{C} = \underset{Y}{C}-$$

$$-\underset{X}{C} = \underset{Y}{C}- + XY \rightarrow -\overset{}{\underset{X \quad X}{C}} \quad \overset{}{\underset{Y \quad Y}{C}}-$$

Addition reactions using potassium permanganate or bromine water are very important in organic chemistry. They are often used for the detection of unsaturated compounds because their addition brings about a clear visible change. An unsaturated compound will decolorize potassium permangante or bromine water [see ethylene, acetylene].

The mechanism of addition reactions

Nucleophilic addition

The carbonyl linkage reacts with nucleophilic reagents. The carbon atom of the carbonyl linkage may adopt a positive charge, and the oxygen atom become negative. Any nucleophilic group will be attracted to the carbon atom, and the intermediate formed in this way may then undergo some rearrangement.

The formation of bisulphite addition products (Experiment 49)

Sodium bisulphite contains bisulphite ions, and these are nucleophilic.

(i) Addition

$$
\underset{\underset{H}{|}}{\overset{+}{C}}-\overset{-}{O} + SO_3H^- \rightarrow \underset{\underset{H}{|}}{\overset{\overset{\displaystyle SO_3H}{|}}{C}}-\overset{-}{O}
$$

(ii) Rearrangement

$$
\underset{\underset{H}{|}}{\overset{\overset{\displaystyle SO_3H}{|}}{C}}-O^- \rightarrow \underset{\underset{H}{|}}{\overset{\overset{\displaystyle SO_3^-}{|}}{C}}-OH
$$

The formation of addition products with ammonia (Experiment 50)

Here the ammonia molecule donates electrons to form an intermediate, which then undergoes rearrangement.

(i)

$$
\underset{\underset{H}{|}}{\overset{+}{C}}-\overset{-}{O} + NH_3 \rightarrow \underset{\underset{H}{|}}{\overset{\overset{\displaystyle +NH_3}{|}}{C}}-O^-
$$

(ii)

$$
\underset{\underset{H}{|}}{\overset{\overset{\displaystyle +NH_3}{|}}{C}}-O^- \rightarrow \underset{\underset{H}{|}}{\overset{\overset{\displaystyle NH_2}{|}}{C}}-OH
$$

Electrophilic addition

There is strong evidence that when ethylene undergoes addition, then its active structure is $H_2\overset{+}{C}$—$\overset{-}{C}H_2$. One of the electron pairs binding the carbon atoms together becomes localized at one of the atoms. There is also strong evidence that addition occurs in two stages. During the first stage an electrophilic group enters the molecule, attacking it at the carbon atom adopting a negative charge. This is followed by the rapid addition of a nucleophilic reagent. When bromine is added to ethylene the mechanism is as follows:

(i)

$$\underset{H}{\overset{H}{>}}C\overset{+}{-}\overset{-}{C}\underset{H}{\overset{H}{<}} + Br_2 \rightarrow \underset{H}{\overset{H}{>}}\overset{+}{C}-C\underset{\underset{Br\quad H}{\diagdown}}{\overset{H}{\diagup}} + Br^-$$

(ii)

$$Br^- + \underset{H}{\overset{H}{>}}\overset{+}{C}-C\underset{\underset{Br\quad H}{\diagup}}{\overset{H}{\diagup}} \rightarrow \underset{\underset{Br\ Br}{\overset{H\ H}{}}}{H-C-C-H}$$

ethylene dibromide

This mechanism has been tested by conducting bromination in the presence of other anions. It is found that when sodium chloride (Na^+Cl^-) is present, then the product contains a little chlorobromo derivative

$$\left(\begin{array}{cc} CH_2-CH_2 \\ | \quad\quad | \\ Br \quad\ Cl \end{array} \right)$$

This would be formed if the intermediate cation $\overset{+}{C}H_2$—CH_2Br reacted with a chloride ion.

Experiment 49. The preparation of benzaldehyde sodium bisulphite

Aldehydes and ketones undergo addition reactions with sodium bisulphite. Sometimes the product is hard to isolate, and benzaldehyde is used because this presents no problem.

$$C_6H_5.CHO + Na^+HSO_3^- \rightarrow C_6H_5.CH(OH).SO_3^-Na^+$$

Method

One-third fill a test-tube with water, and add sodium bisulphite until the solution is saturated. Add a few drops of benzaldehyde, cork the tube, and shake it vigorously. Observe the formation of white crystals of benzaldehyde sodium bisulphite, and note that the reaction is exothermic.

Experiment 50. The addition of acetaldehyde and ammonia

$$CH_3 . CHO + NH_3 \rightarrow CH_3 . CH(OH) . NH_2$$
$$\text{acetaldehyde ammonia}$$

Pour a few millilitres of 0·88 ammonia into a conical flask. Wet the interior of a second flask with acetaldehyde and then invert it, placing it mouth to mouth over the one containing the ammonia. Observe the white fumes and the slow formation of tiny crystals of acetaldehyde ammonia on the walls of the upper flask. Note that the reaction is exothermic; the upper flask becomes warm.

Experiment 51. The preparation of ethylene, and its addition products with bromine and chlorine

Ethylene is prepared by the dehydration of ethyl alcohol, and the dehydrating agent used is hot concentrated sulphuric acid.

$$C_2H_5OH - H_2O \rightarrow C_2H_4$$

Place 20 ml of industrial alcohol in a round-bottomed flask, and add to this 40 ml of concentrated sulphuric acid. The addition must be slow and the flask cooled under the tap. Now set up the apparatus shown in fig. 33, placing dilute sodium hydroxide in the *second wash-bottle* so that sulphur dioxide may be removed. Add a little silver sand to the alcohol–acid mixture to ensure a steady evolution of ethylene, then heat the flask on a sand-bath. Collect the gas by displacement of water.

Tests on jars of the gas.—(i). Add a few millilitres of bromine water, replace the cover slide, and shake the jar. Note the rapid decolorization.

$$C_2H_4 + Br_2 \rightarrow C_2H_4Br_2 \quad \text{[ethylene dibromide]}$$

and $C_2H_4 + HOBr \rightarrow C_2H_4(OH).Br \quad \text{[ethylene bromohydrin]}$

(ii). Add a few millilitres of dilute potassium permanganate solution made alkaline with sodium hydroxide solution. Shake the jar and observe the colour change.

(iii) and (iv). Repeat (ii) but use acidified and then neutral potassium permanganate.

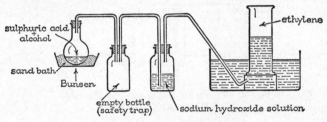

Fig. 33.—The preparation of ethylene

Notes.—In these reactions, the addition product is ethylene glycol $CH_2(OH).CH_2(OH)$. The permanganate ion is reduced, and in the presence of alkalis the manganate ion is formed. Manganate salts are green.

$$MnO_4^- + e \rightarrow MnO_4^{--}$$

In presence of acids, manganous salts are produced, and these are almost colourless.

$$MnO_4^- + 8H^+ + 5e \rightarrow Mn^{++} + 4H_2O$$

Neutral solutions produce the insoluble manganese dioxide.

$$MnO_4^- + 4H^+ + 3e \rightarrow MnO_2 + 2H_2O$$

(v). Fill a beaker with brine, and invert in it a graduated tube, also full of brine. Displace half the brine in the tube with ethylene gas, and the remainder with chlorine. Observe that brine rises up the tube as addition occurs to form an insoluble liquid.

$$C_2H_4 + Cl_2 \rightarrow C_2H_4.Cl_2$$
$$\text{ethylene dichloride}$$

Experiment 52. *The preparation of ethylene dibromide*

Use the method described for the preparation of ethylene (fig. 33) but replace the trough by two wash-bottles, connected as shown in fig. 34. Set up the apparatus in a fume cupboard. Add 10 ml of bromine to each bottle (CAUTION—*wear rubber gloves*), and then introduce 10 ml of water into each, so that the bromine is

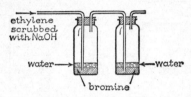

Fig. 34.—The preparation of ethylene dibromide
(FUME CUPBOARD)

covered with a layer of water. Generate ethylene, and allow it to bubble through the bromine. Continue until the colour of bromine is discharged. Disconnect the apparatus, and transfer the contents of both bottles into a separating funnel. Collect the lower layer, wash it with water, then with sodium carbonate solution, finally with water. Place the product, together with a little anhydrous calcium chloride, in a stoppered tube. Allow it to dry for $\frac{1}{2}$ h. Decant the ethylene dibromide into a small flask, and distil it using a small flame applied directly, collecting the liquid which boils at 130–135°C. Measure the yield.

Experiment 53. *The addition of bromine to benzene*

$$C_6H_6 + 3Br_2 \rightarrow C_6H_6Br_6$$

Place a little bromine in a 50-ml beaker, and cover it with a layer of benzene. Set the beaker in a desiccator, and expose it to sunlight for a few days. Observe the formation of crystalline benzene hexabromide.

Dehydration Reactions

13

Calcium chloride, calcium oxide, sulphuric acid, phosphorus pentoxide, and metallic sodium are widely used as drying agents. Their suitability for a particular job must be assessed carefully. Liquids are often dried by placing agents in contact with them, and there must be no chemical reaction between the desiccant and the liquid. After drying, the liquid must be separated from the desiccant, and the latter must be chosen so that this operation is easy. The physical condition of a drying agent affects the drying time. A fine powder presents greater surface area (sodium wire is preferred for the same reason) but the physical state must not lead to a difficult separation. Removal of water can never be complete and the desiccant comes to equilibrium with the residual water. Each desiccant dries to a different extent, and the one chosen must produce a material which is dry enough for a specific use. If we wish to study the action of phosphorus pentachloride on an alcohol, the water content of the latter must be lower than that tolerated in a study of the action of acetic acid on the same.

When a dehydrating agent removes 'the elements of water' from a compound, and leads to the formation of a new compound, then the process is termed a dehydration *reaction*. This must not be confused with the process of drying. The dehydration products may vary according to the conditions of the reaction. Temperature and the proportion of dehydrating agent are often very important. The products and conditions for a number of standard dehydrations are listed overleaf.

(i)   alcohols $\xrightarrow[\text{high temperature}]{\text{high proportion } H_2SO_4}$ olefines

e.g. $\underset{\text{ethyl alcohol}}{C_2H_5OH}$ $\longrightarrow$ $\underset{\text{ethylene}}{C_2H_4 + H_2O}$

(ii)   alcohols $\xrightarrow[\text{low temperature}]{\text{low proportion } H_2SO_4}$ ethers

e.g. $2C_2H_5OH$ $\longrightarrow$ $\underset{\text{diethyl ether}}{(C_2H_5)_2O + H_2O}$

(iii)   amides $\xrightarrow[\text{heat}]{P_2O_5}$ nitriles

e.g. $\underset{\text{acetamide}}{CH_3.CO.NH_2}$ $\longrightarrow$ $\underset{\text{acetonitrile}}{CH_3.CN + H_2O}$

(iv)   ammonium salts of
       fatty acids $\xrightarrow{\text{heat}}$ amides

e.g. $\underset{\text{ammonium acetate}}{CH_3.COO^-NH_4^+}$ $\longrightarrow$ $\underset{\text{acetamide}}{CH_3.CO.NH_2 + H_2O}$

(v)   carboxylic acids $\xrightarrow{\text{heat}}$ acid anhydrides

$$2R.COOH \rightarrow (R.CO)_2O + H_2O$$

Experiment 54. The dehydration of cane sugar

$$C_{12}H_{22}O_{11} \rightarrow 12C + 11H_2O$$

Place a few crystals of sugar in a boiling-tube. Add a little concentrated sulphuric acid and warm gently. Note the formation of carbon.

Experiment 55. The dehydration of formic acid

$$H.COOH \rightarrow CO + H_2O$$

Place a few millilitres of concentrated sulphuric acid in a test-tube. Add a few drops of formic acid, warm the tube gently, and light the gas evolved. Note the characteristic carbon monoxide flame.

Experiment 56. The dehydration of oxalic acid

$$(COOH)_2 \rightarrow CO + CO_2 + H_2O$$

Add concentrated sulphuric acid to oxalic acid in a test-tube. Warm the tube gently and note the evolution of carbon monoxide and carbon dioxide. The former burns with a blue flame; the latter turns lime-water cloudy.

Repeat this experiment with tartaric acid and citric acid.

For the dehydration of alcohol to olefine see Experiment 51.

Experiment 57. The preparation of diethyl ether

CAUTION. *Ether vapour is highly inflammable and forms explosive mixtures when mixed with air. Do the experiment in a fume cupboard.*

Cover the bottom of a three-necked flask with silver sand. Pour 7 ml of industrial alcohol into the flask, and then slowly add 5½ ml of concentrated sulphuric acid, cooling the flask under the

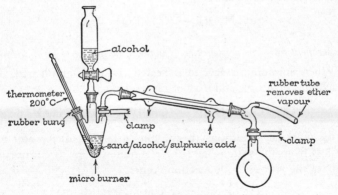

Fig. 35.—The preparation of diethyl ether

tap. Set the flask as shown in fig. 35, using a thermometer reading to 200°C. Connect the side-arm of the receiver to a length of rubber tubing and set the open end of this in a sink. The rubber tube carries vapour below bench level, so that it does not come into contact with a flame. Place 7 ml of industrial alcohol in the dropping funnel and heat the flask until the contents are at 140°C; add alcohol from the funnel at the same rate as ether distils over. If the alcohol is added too quickly, then it will distil over unchanged.

When addition is completed, extinguish all flames; and then transfer the crude ether to a separating funnel. Shake the ether with sodium hydroxide solution, periodically releasing the pressure, so that acidic impurities are removed (SO_2). Run off and discard the lower layer. Shake the ether with water to remove any alkali and alcohol which remain. Transfer the ether to a test-tube containing a little anhydrous calcium chloride, cork the tube, and allow the ether to dry for 30 min. Decant the dry ether into a distilling flask, and collect the fraction boiling at 34–38°C (fig. 4). For this final distillation use a water-bath, and lead ether vapour away from any flame by means of a length of rubber tube connected to the receiver.

Measure the yield and compare this with the theoretical value obtained from the equation

$$2C_2H_5OH \rightarrow (C_2H_5)_2O + H_2O$$

Experiment 58. The dehydration of ammonium acetate to form acetamide

When ammonium acetate is heated, water is eliminated. The reaction is reversible and may be represented as

$$CH_3.COO^-NH_4^+ \rightleftharpoons CH_3.CO.NH_2 + H_2O$$

If the working conditions are carefully arranged, then water may be lost from the system, and the reaction will go to completion. During the process a side reaction occurs:

$$CH_3OCO^-NH_4^+ \rightarrow CH_3COOH + NH_3$$

This is repressed by conducting the dehydration in the presence of glacial acetic acid.

Method

Place 5 g of ammonium acetate and 6 ml of glacial acetic acid in a pear-shaped flask. Fill an air condenser with pieces of glass rod (4–5 mm long) by placing a finger at one end to cover the cone, and introducing the pieces at the other until they lodge in the tube. Set the column in position on the flask, and cap the condenser with a glass bend, as shown in fig. 36. Arrange a test-tube to collect the acetic acid/water distillate. Heat the flask using a small flame, so that distillate is collected very slowly (one drop every 15 s). Continue

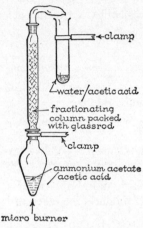

Fig. 36.—The preparation of acetamide

the heating for 45 min. Now connect the flask for normal distillation using an air condenser (fig. 9). Heat the flask using a small flame, and when the temperature is 190°C, change the receiver and collect the acetamide at 190–230°C. The product melts at 82°C and might crystallize in the condenser. This may be overcome by fanning the condenser with a small flame. Should the product fail to crystallize in the receiver, introduce a seed crystal of acetamide.

Reactions of acetamide

1. For the conversion to methylamine see Experiment 81.
2. For the action of alkalis see Experiment 19 (1).

$$CH_3CO . NH_2 + OH^- \rightarrow CH_3COO^- + NH_3$$

3. *Nitrous acid reaction*

$$CH_3.CO.NH_2 + HNO_2 \rightarrow CH_3.COOH + N_2 + H_2O$$

Prepare a few millilitres of concentrated sodium nitrite solution and cool it in ice. Add a little dilute acetic acid and allow any evolution of gas to subside. Now add the mixture to a cold aqueous solution of acetamide. Note the evolution of nitrogen.

4. Dehydration to acetonitrile (see Experiment 60).

5. Hydrolysis (see Experiment 63).

Experiment 59. The preparation of succinic anhydride

The direct heating of a dibasic acid may lead to a loss of water, and the formation of an anhydride.

$$\begin{matrix} CH_2.COOH \\ | \\ CH_2.COOH \end{matrix} \xrightarrow{\text{heat}} \begin{matrix} CH_2.CO \\ | \\ CH_2.CO \end{matrix} \!\!\!\!\searrow\!\!\!\nearrow O$$

succinic acid   succinic anhydride

The conversion is much more efficient if a dehydrating agent is used; acetic anhydride produces the reaction

$$(CH_2)_2.(COOH)_2 + (CH_3.CO)_2O$$
$$\rightarrow (CH_2.CO)_2O + 2.CH_3.COOH$$

The acetic anhydride removes water and is converted to acetic acid.

Method

Place 2 g of succinic acid in a pear-shaped flask and add 4 ml of fresh acetic anhydride. Attach a water condenser to the flask, in the reflux position, and guard the top of the condenser with a calcium chloride tube (fig. 37). Heat the flask on a water-bath until a clear solution is obtained, and then continue the reflux for one hour. Allow the flask to cool in ice, leaving the condenser in position. Filter the crystals of succinic anhydride at a pump, and wash them with dry ether. Weigh the yield and compare it with the theoretical value obtained from the equation.

Test-tube reactions of anhydrides (use acetic anhydride)

1. As an acetylating agent (see Experiment 46).
2. Repeat Experiment 46 but use ethyl alcohol instead of aniline. Ethyl acetate is formed.

Experiment 60. The preparation of acetonitrile

$$\underset{\text{acetamide}}{CH_3 . CO . NH_2} \underset{P_2O_5}{\rightarrow} CH_3CN + \text{acids of phosphorus}$$

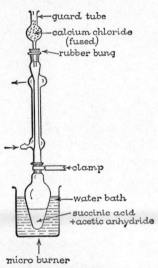

Fig. 37.—The preparation of succinic anhydride

CAUTION: *Phosphorus pentoxide must not come into contact with the skin.*

Thoroughly dry a pear-shaped flask and introduce 1·5 g of acetamide. Weigh out 2 g of phosphorus pentoxide on a piece of paper and transfer it to the flask. Mix the chemicals with a glass rod. *Note.*—The weighing and the introduction of phosphorus pentoxide must be carried out quickly. It absorbs water from the air very rapidly.

Connect the flask to a water condenser and heat the flask with a small flame (see fig. 25). The main impurity in the distillate is acetic acid, formed by the action of phosphoric acid on acetamide. Transfer the distillate to a separating funnel and wash it with saturated potassium carbonate solution. Recover the upper layer, transfer it to a distilling flask, add a little phosphorus pentoxide, connect a condenser and thermometer as shown in fig. 4, and collect the liquid which boils at 78–85°C.

Hydrolysis Reactions

14

When a compound is decomposed by water, then it is said to be hydrolysed, and the compounds formed are called hydrolysis products. This class of reaction is a very important one, and the influence of temperature and of catalysts has been studied in great detail. Amongst the latter, acids and alkalis are often used. Again, the reversibility of many hydrolysis reactions has been the subject of careful study. In preparative work, the main problem is to force a reaction to completion, and this is often done by the addition of a reagent which reacts with a hydrolysis product.

A number of important hydrolysis reactions are given below in general terms.

(i)   ester + water → acid + alcohol

$$R.COOR^1 + H_2O \rightarrow R.COOH + R^1OH$$

(ii)   amide + water → ammonium salt

$$R.CO.NH_2 + H_2O \rightarrow R.COO^-NH_4^+$$

(iii)   nitrile + H_2O → amide

$$R.CN + H_2O \rightarrow R.CO.NH_2$$

(iv)   acid chloride + H_2O → acid + hydrochloric acid

$$R.CO.Cl + H_2O \rightarrow R.COOH + HCl$$

(v)   acid anhydride + H_2O → acid

$$(R.CO)_2O + H_2O \rightarrow 2R.COOH$$

(vi)   alkyl halide + H_2O → alcohol + hydracid

$$RX + H_2O \rightarrow R.OH + HX$$

or, under different conditions,

            alkyl halide + H_2O → olefine + hydracid

(vii)   disaccharides + H_2O → saccharides

$$C_{12}H_{22}O_{11} + H_2O \rightarrow 2C_6H_{12}O_6$$

(viii) The peptide linkage (—CO—NH—) is broken:

$$R—CO—NH—R^1 + H_2O \rightarrow R—COOH + NH_2—R^1$$
$$\text{carboxylic acid} \quad \text{amine}$$

Mechanism

In many cases hydrolysis works by the formation of an intermediate addition product. This then suffers a rearrangement to give the products with which we are familiar. Water molecules are nucleophilic (see p. 76), each one containing electron pairs which may be donated. Acid chlorides, anhydrides, peptides, amides, and esters have molecules containing a carbonyl group $\diagup C=O$. Within this group there is some delocalization of an electron pair and the group behaves as a dipole $\diagup \overset{+}{C}—\overset{-}{O}$ (see p. 79). A water molecule attacks this linkage at the carbon atom, and the intermediate is formed

The mechanism of the hydrolysis of esters depends upon the acidity of the system.

1. *In acid*

2. *In alkali* (NaOH)

(The sodium salt of a fatty acid is formed.)

Experiment 61. The hydrolysis of phenylbenzoate

Esters are hydrolysed with the formation of their constituent acids and alcohols. The process is important in commerce because the products are useful; soap and glycerol result from the hydrolysis of fat. The process is important in chemical research, because an ester of unknown structure may be characterized by hydrolysing it, isolating the products, and identifying them. Phenylbenzoate is used to illustrate the method because its hydrolysis products are easy to isolate and identify.

The phenylbenzoate is refluxed with sodium hydroxide solution and this produces a mixture of sodium benzoate and sodium phenate, both of which are water-soluble.

$$C_6H_5 . COOC_6H_5 + 2OH^- \rightarrow C_6H_5 . COO^- + C_6H_5O^- + H_2O$$

Acidification of the resulting solution gives the free acid and phenol, and these are sparingly soluble in water.

$$C_6H_5 . COO^- + H^+ \rightarrow C_6H_5 . COOH \text{ (benzoic acid)}$$
$$C_6H_5O^- + H^+ \rightarrow C_6H_5 . OH \text{ (phenol)}$$

The addition of sodium carbonate causes the benzoic acid to react and dissolve as sodium benzoate, whilst the phenol fails to react and is removed by ether extraction.

$$2C_6H_5COOH + CO_3^{--} \rightarrow 2C_6H_5COO^- + H_2O + CO_2$$

Method

Place 1 g of phenylbenzoate in a pear-shaped flask and introduce 12 ml of 10% sodium hydroxide solution. Attach a water condenser to the flask, in the reflux position, and boil the mixture using a micro burner until the ester disappears. Cool the flask in cold water and then add dilute sulphuric acid until the mixture is acidic (test with litmus). Now add sodium carbonate solution until the solution is slightly alkaline (the precipitate dissolves). Transfer the cold solution to a separating funnel and extract it with two lots of ether, collecting the ether in a beaker. CAUTION: *Ether is inflammable, and mixed with air is explosive. Avoid naked flames.* Evaporate the ether in a fume cupboard using a water-bath. Phenol remains.

Next acidify the solution which has been extracted, filter off the crystals of benzoic acid at a pump, wash them with water, and dry them in a desiccator. Determine the melting point (122°C).

Reactions of phenol

1. *Reduction.* See Experiment 24.

2. *Bromine water.* See Experiment 75.

3. *Nitration.* See Experiment 76.

4. *Ferric chloride.* Dissolve a little phenol in water, add one drop of ferric chloride solution, and observe the coloration. The ferric chloride solution must be neutral (page 63).

5. *Liebermann reaction.* Place 0·5 g of phenol in a clean dry test-tube, and add a small crystal of sodium nitrite. Heat the tube gently for half a minute, allow it to cool, and then add twice the volume of concentrated sulphuric acid. Mix the contents by rotating the tube. Observe the slow development of a green-blue colour. Dilute with water (CAUTION) and the solution turns red. On addition of excess sodium hydroxide solution the solution reverts to a blue-green colour.

6. *Phthalein reaction.* See Experiment 42.

7. *Azo dye reaction.* See Experiment 41.

8. *Sodium carbonate solution.* Add a few crystals of phenol to sodium carbonate solution. Note that no carbon dioxide is evolved. Compare this with the behaviour of carboxylic acids using acetic and benzoic acids.

9. *Benzoylation. The Schotten-Baumann reaction.*

CAUTION: *Wear goggles when performing this reaction, and transfer the benzoyl chloride in a fume cupboard.*

Place 1 g of phenol in a boiling-tube, and add 10 ml of bench sodium hydroxide. Add 2 ml of benzoyl chloride, cork the tube, and shake it until the solid derivative, phenyl benzoate, is formed

$$C_6H_5OH + OH^- \rightarrow C_6H_5O^- + H_2O$$

$$\underset{\text{benzoyl chloride}}{C_6H_5O^- + C_6H_5 . CO . Cl} \rightarrow \underset{\text{phenylbenzoate}}{C_6H_5O . CO . C_6H_5} + Cl^-$$

Experiment 62. The saponification of fat to produce soap

Fats are esters of the trihydric alcohol, glycerol, with carboxylic acids of high molecular weight. Stearic acid is often present and has the formula $C_{17}H_{35} . COOH$. A fat might have the formula $(C_{17}H_{35} . COO)_3C_3H_5$, and its saponification may be written:

$$\begin{array}{l}
CH_2 . OOC . C_{17}H_{35} \\
| \\
CH . OOC . C_{17}H_{35} + 3Na^+OH^- \rightarrow \\
| \\
CH_2 . OOC . C_{17}H_{35}
\end{array}
\begin{array}{l}
CH_2 . OH \\
| \\
CH . OH + 3C_{17}H_{35} . COO^-Na^+ \\
| \qquad\qquad\qquad \text{sodium stearate} \\
CH_2 . OH \qquad\qquad\quad \text{'soap'} \\
\text{glycerol}
\end{array}$$

After saponification, the soap may be isolated by adding sodium chloride. The sodium ion is common to salt and soap, and its introduction reduces the solubility of the soap. Free stearic acid may be obtained by acidifying the soap,

$$C_{17}H_{35} . COO^- + H^+ \rightarrow C_{17}H_{35} . COOH$$

Method

Place 1 g of lard in an evaporating dish, add 1 g of sodium hydroxide and 10 ml of methyl alcohol. Stir the mixture well and heat it on a water-bath until a semi-solid mass of soap and glycerol remains. Dissolve the mixture in the minimum amount of warm water and divide the solution into two parts. To one part add brine and observe the precipitation of soap. To the other add dilute hydrochloric acid and observe the formation of free acid.

Filter off the soap, wash it with water, and then dissolve it in warm water. Test the 'soapiness' of the solution by rubbing it between the fingers, by bubbling air through it, and by adding it to hard water. Filter the free acid, allow it to dry in a desiccator. Dissolve it in carbon tetrachloride, and add a few drops of bromine water. The decolorization is caused by an unsaturated acid and not by stearic acid.

Experiment 63. The hydrolysis of acetamide

$$CH_3.CO.NH_2 + OH^- \rightarrow CH_3.COO^- + NH_3$$
$$\text{acetate ions}$$

Put a little acetamide into a test–tube, add sodium hydroxide solution and warm the tube. Test for ammonia using a glass rod wet with concentrated hydrochloric acid. Observe the slow evolution of ammonia and compare this with the evolution from ammonium acetate under similar conditions.

Experiment 64. The hydrolysis of acetyl chloride

CAUTION: *Acetyl chloride vapour is very toxic and the reaction is violent. Wear rubber gloves and work in a fume cupboard.*

$$CH_3.CO.Cl + H_2O \rightarrow CH_3.COOH + HCl$$

Add a few drops of acetyl chloride to a test-tube containing water. Observe that the reaction is fast and very exothermic. Test for hydrogen chloride using a glass rod, wet with 0·88 ammonia. Repeat the experiment with acetic anhydride; observe that there is little reaction.

Experiment 65. The hydrolysis of cane sugar

$$C_{12}H_{22}O_{11} + H_2O \rightarrow C_6H_{12}O_6 + C_6H_{12}O_6$$
$$\text{glucose} \qquad \text{fructose}$$

Prepare a dilute solution of cane sugar and divide it into two portions. To one add Fehling's solution and warm the mixture. Observe that little or no reduction occurs. To the other portion add a few drops of dilute sulphuric acid and boil the solution. Next cool the solution and make it slightly alkaline by adding a few drops of sodium hydroxide solution. Add Fehling's solution and warm the mixture. Observe that the reagent is now reduced. The cane sugar has been hydrolysed to glucose and fructose, which are reducing sugars.

Experiment 66. The hydrolysis of acetanilide

$$C_6H_5 . NH . CO . CH_3 + H_2O + H^+$$
acetanilide
$$Cl^-$$
$$\rightarrow C_6H_5 . NH_3^+ + CH_3 . COOH$$
$$Cl^-$$
aniline hydrochloride

If the resulting solution is made alkaline, free aniline is produced,

$$C_6H_5NH_3^+ + OH^- \rightarrow C_6H_5NH_2 + H_2O$$

When proteins are boiled with acids, they are hydrolysed in a similar manner. Water molecules attack the protein at peptide linkages (—NH—CO—), but the hydrolysis products are very difficult to isolate.

Method

Boil a little acetanilide with a few millilitres of concentrated hydrochloric acid for a minute. Pour the product into a boiling-tube containing cold water. Make the solution alkaline with sodium hydroxide solution and observe the formation of aniline. Test this by adding sodium hypochlorite solution. A purple coloration is produced.

Substitution Reactions

15

If, during the course of a chemical reaction, atoms or groups of atoms in an organic molecule are replaced by other atoms or groups, then a substitution reaction has occurred, and the derivative is called a *substitution product*. This type of reaction may be presented in the general form

$$RX + AB \rightarrow RA + XB$$

R being a radical containing carbon atoms. X might be a hydrogen atom as in methane $CH_3.H$ and benzene $C_6H_5.H$. Or it might be a hydroxyl group as in the alcohols or fatty acids. A and B may be identical as in the case of a chlorine molecule, or they may differ as in the cases of HCl, H_2SO_4, HNO_3. RA is called the *substitution product*. A number of important substitution reactions are listed below:

(*a*) *Nitration*

Nitration is the substitution of one or more hydrogen atoms in a molecule by nitro groups ($—NO_2$).

$$RH + HNO_3 \rightarrow \underset{\text{nitro compound}}{R.NO_2} + H_2O$$

(*b*) *Sulphonation*

The substitution of one or more hydrogen atoms in a molecule by sulphonic acid groups ($—SO_3H$).

$$RH + H_2SO_4 \rightarrow \underset{\text{a sulphonic acid}}{R.SO_3H} + H_2O$$

(c) Halogenation

The introduction of halogen atoms into a molecule.

Hydrocarbon $\quad R.H + Br_2 \rightarrow R.Br + HBr$

Alcohol $\quad\quad R.OH + HI \rightarrow R.I + H_2O$

acid $\quad\quad\quad 3R.COOH + PCl_3 \rightarrow 3R.COCl + H_3PO_3$

(d) Introduction of nitrile groups.

Alkyl halide $\quad R.Br + KCN \rightarrow R.CN + KBr$

(e) Introduction of amino groups.

$$R.Br + NH_3 \rightarrow R.NH_2 + HBr$$

(f) Introduction of metals.

$$2R.OH + 2Na \rightarrow 2RO^-Na^+ + H_2$$

The mechanism of substitution reactions

The conditions of substitution are of critical importance; they influence the rate of reaction, the kind of intermediate compound formed, and often the nature of the final product. The reaction of a substance A with another B might give rise to a number of products C, D, E, each product resulting from a particular mechanism *c, d, e.*

$$A + B \overset{c}{\rightarrow} C$$

$$A + B \overset{d}{\rightarrow} D$$

$$A + B \overset{e}{\rightarrow} E$$

If D is required, then conditions must be such that mechanism *d* takes place much faster than the other possibilities. Of the conditions under our control, the nature of the solvent, the temperature, the concentrations of the reactants, and the duration of reaction need consideration.

The nature of the solvent

When an alkyl halide reacts with an alkali, then the reaction may be expressed as
$$RX + OH^- \rightarrow \underset{\text{alcohol}}{ROH} + X^-$$

Good yields of alcohol are obtained if the reaction is conducted in water. If alcoholic solutions are used, and other conditions are similar, then olefines are often produced. In the case of *n*-propyl iodide

(a) $C_3H_7I + OH^- \xrightarrow[\text{solvent}]{\text{water}} C_3H_7OH + I^-$

(b) $C_3H_7I + OH^- \xrightarrow[\text{solvent}]{\text{methyl alcohol}} \underset{\text{propylene}}{C_3H_6} + H_2O + I^-$

A mixed solvent yields both products, the proportions of methyl alcohol/water in the solvent influencing the rates (a) and (b) (fig. 38).

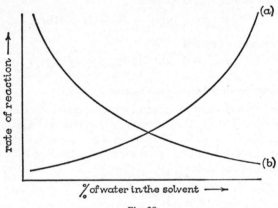

Fig. 38

Water encourages reaction by a mechanism:

(i) $RX \rightarrow R^+ + X^-$ (ionization)

(ii) $R^+ + OH^- \rightarrow ROH$ (association)

This reaction is also encouraged if the radical —R is nucleophilic. Such a group is prone to yield electrons and the ionization stage is encouraged.

Methanol will repress ionization, and the reaction works via an intermediate compound; this then undergoes rearrangement and an olefine may be formed

$$OH^- + RX \rightarrow (OH—R—X)^-   \text{(intermediate)}$$

Aromatic substitution

The stability of benzene presents a problem which has received a great deal of study. The classical structure used to represent the molecule (1a) is quite inadequate for explaining the observed properties of the compound. An inspection of 1a leads to the prediction that benzene will be a highly unsaturated compound—it should undergo addition reactions very readily. In fact, benzene resists addition; its dominant property is that it is readily substituted. Hydrogen atoms attached to the carbon ring may be replaced easily.

Substitution comes about because three pairs of electrons, represented as bonds between carbon atoms in 1a, are in fact delocalized 1b (see p. 72). If some influence does cause such a pair to become localized at a carbon atom, then this will attract any electrophilic group ($\oplus$). Conversely, any electrophilic group $\oplus$ in the locality of a carbon atom, will attract an electron pair to this atom, leaving another part of the benzene molecule positively charged (1c).

1a	1b	1c
All electrons localized	Three electron pairs delocalized	The influence of an electrophilic group

Electrophilic substitution

In many cases the benzene molecule is attacked by electrophilic reagents, and conditions are chosen so that the electrophilic reagent is in liberal supply. An intermediate addition product is formed and elimination follows.

Nitration (Experiments 67 and 68)

Nitric acid is often used as a nitrating agent, and the reaction is conducted in the presence of concentrated sulphuric acid. The solvent encourages the

ionization shown in equation (1). The nitro group undergoes an addition
with a molecule of benzene (2), and elimination follows (3).

(1) $H^+ + HNO_3 \rightarrow H_2O + NO_2^+$

(2) $NO_2^+ +$ (intermediate)

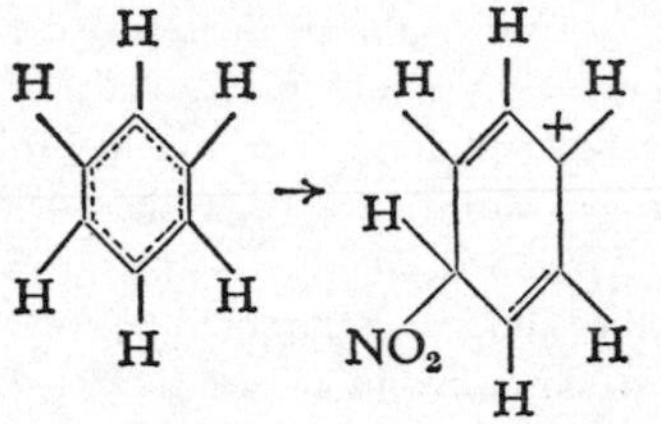

(3) $+ H^+$

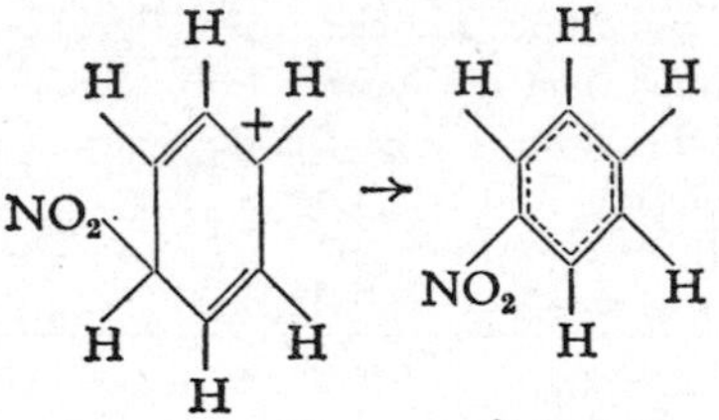

nitrobenzene

Halogenation

Hydrogen atoms in the benzene molecule may be replaced by halogen
atoms in the presence of certain catalysts. It is characteristic of these catalysts
that they are electrophilic, and because of this they bring about the ionization of the halogen molecules, yielding positive ions. The positive ions
formed are electrophilic and substitute in the benzene ring.

(i) $Cl_2 + AlCl_3 \rightarrow Cl^+ + (AlCl_4)^-$
                         (catalyst)

(ii) $Cl^+ +$ (intermediate)

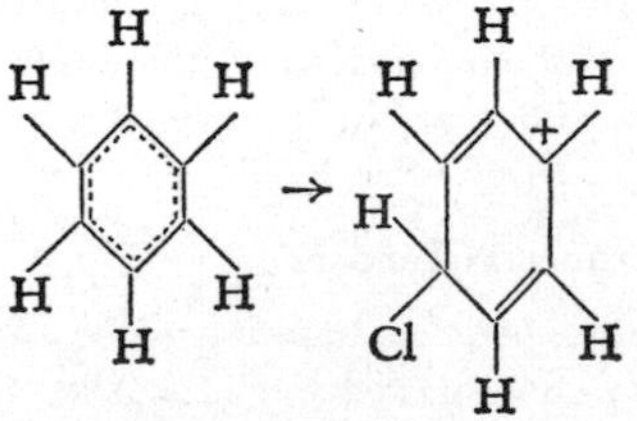

(iii)

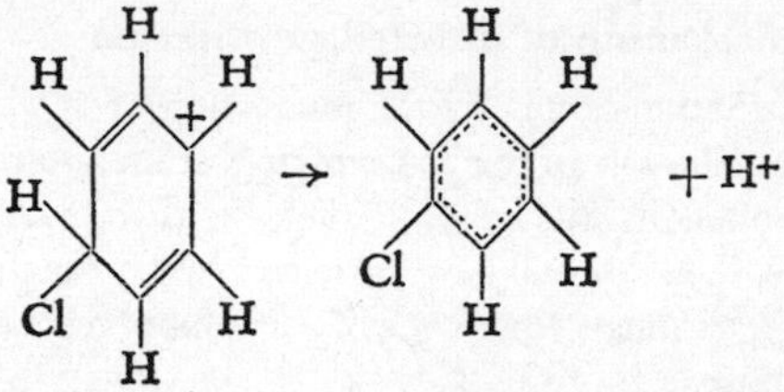

chlorobenzene

Directed substitution

When benzene has been substituted by a group X, and further substitution of $C_6H_5 \cdot X$ is attempted, then X influences the rate and the position of the substitution. Structure 1a shows how carbon atoms are labelled in this work, and chart 1b shows how X directs and influences the rate of further substitution. Some experimental evidence may be found in Experiments 68, 74, and 75.

1a

The labelling of $C_6H_5 \cdot X$

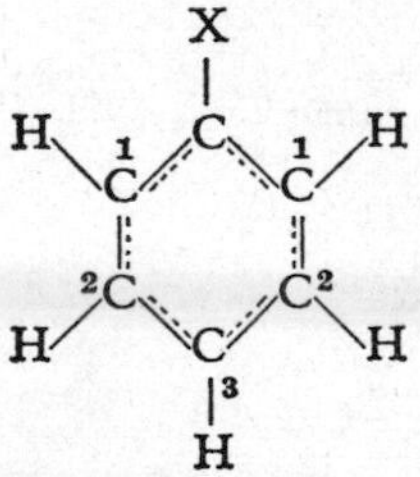

1. Carbons in the *ortho* position.
2. Carbons in the *meta* position.
3. Carbon in the *para* position.

1b

Group X	Directs further substitution	Rate of further substitution, relative to that for the substitution of benzene
—NH₂ (amino)	ortho and para	much faster
—OH (phenol)	ortho and para	much faster
—halogen	ortho and para	slightly faster
—NO₂ (nitro)	meta	slower

The mechanism of directed substitution

Substitution occurs by the interaction of an electrophilic reagent with a nucleophilic part of the benzene ring. If the group X influences the electron distribution in the benzene ring, so that nucleophilic centres are more intense, then this will have the effect of speeding up substitution. Similarly, if X determines where the nucleophilic centres are, then it will direct substitution.

Ortho-para directing groups

A common feature of these is that they are able to denote an electron pair to the carbon structure.

Phenol may adopt the distributions shown in 1a; aniline may adopt similar distributions 1b. In these, carbon atoms in the ortho and para positions become negative, and it is in these positions that rapid substitution occurs. The products, tribromophenol and tribromoaniline are formed rapidly when bromine water is added to phenol and aniline respectively (1c). (See Experiments 74 and 75.)

1a

phenol C$_6$H$_5$.OH

1b

aniline C$_6$H$_5$.NH$_2$

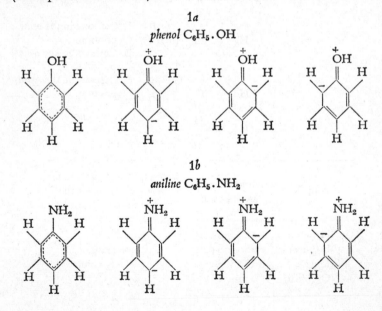

1c

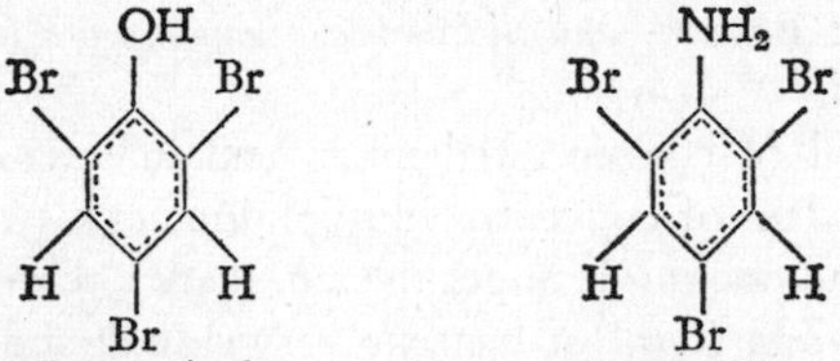

OH
Br   Br

H   H

Br
tribromophenol

NH₂
Br   Br

H   H

Br
tribromoaniline

Meta directing groups

These slow down substitution by withdrawing electrons from the benzene ring. In this process, carbon atoms in the ortho and para positions become positively charged and an electrophilic reagent is directed to the meta positions. Nitrobenzene may adopt the structures:

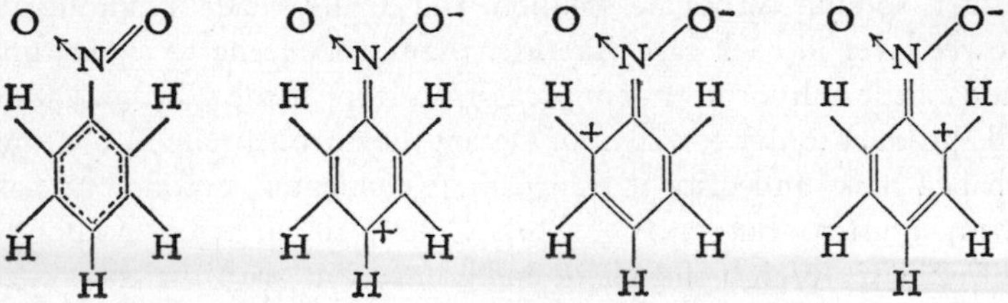

Experiment 67. The preparation of nitrobenzene

$$C_6H_6 + HNO_3 \rightarrow C_6H_5 . NO_2 + H_2O$$

In the preparation of nitrobenzene it is very important to prevent the temperature rising above 55°C. Above this a secondary reaction occurs to a considerable extent, and meta dinitrobenzene is formed:

$$C_6H_5 . NO_2 + HNO_3 \rightarrow C_6H_4(NO_2)_2 + H_2O$$

The nitrating mixture consists of nitric and sulphuric acids, and some sulphonation will occur, though not to any great extent.

Method

CAUTION: *Benzene and nitrobenzene vapours are toxic. Work in a fume cupboard.*

Place 12 ml of concentrated nitric acid in a 250-ml flask, and slowly add 12 ml of concentrated sulphuric acid, swirling the flask constantly and cooling it under the tap. Place a thermometer in the mixture and add 10 ml of benzene very slowly and with constant agitation. During the mixing, the temperature should not rise above 50°C; the flask must be cooled in cold water. When addition is complete, stand the flask in a water-bath at 55°C and allow the reaction to continue for 45 min. At frequent intervals remove the flask and mix the contents by shaking it gently. Cool the mixture and transfer it to a beaker of water, stirring vigorously. The nitrobenzene forms a lower layer. Decant off as much water as possible, and separate the rest using a tap funnel. Wash the nitrobenzene with water, sodium carbonate solution, and finally water, retaining the lower layer in each case. Transfer the nitrobenzene to a test-tube, add a little anhydrous calcium chloride, stopper the tube, and allow the product to dry for 20 min. Decant the nitrobenzene into a pear-shaped flask, and distil it using an air condenser, heating the flask with a micro burner (fig. 21*d*). Collect the fraction boiling at 207–211°C. Weigh the yield, and compare it with the theoretical value obtained from the equation for the reaction.

Experiment 68. The preparation of meta dinitrobenzene

$$C_6H_5 . NO_2 + HNO_3 \rightarrow C_6H_4(NO_2)_2 + H_2O$$

CAUTION: *Wear rubber gloves and work in a fume cupboard. Fuming nitric acid is extremely corrosive.*

Place 2 ml of fuming nitric acid in a pear-shaped flask, add to this 2½ ml of concentrated sulphuric acid slowly and with shaking. Add a piece of porous pot, and then attach an air condenser to the flask in the reflux position. Slowly add 1½ ml of nitrobenzene through the air condenser. ADDITION OF THE NITRO-BENZENE MUST BE SLOW, AND THE FLASK MUST BE

SHAKEN AFTER EACH ADDITION. Heat the flask on a boiling-water bath for 30 min. Cool the flask and then pour the contents into a beaker of cold water, stirring the water vigorously. Filter the crystals of meta dinitrobenzene at a pump, and wash them with cold water. Recrystallize the product from industrial spirit (see Experiment 4). Measure the melting point and the yield of the product. Compare the latter with the theoretical value obtained from the equation.

Experiment 69. The preparation of para-xylene sulphonic acid

$$C_6H_4(CH_3)_2 + H_2SO_4 \rightarrow C_6H_3(CH_3)_2 . SO_3H + H_2O$$

The sulphonation of benzene is slow, a high temperature is required, and the benzene sulphonic acid is difficult to isolate. The hydrocarbon *p*-xylene, on the other hand, is easy to sulphonate. The reaction takes place quickly at 80°C, and the product is easy to isolate. In addition to these advantages, *p*-xylene forms one mono substitution product only. It must have the structure

Method

Place 4 ml of *p*-xylene in a dry test-tube. Add 6 ml of concentrated sulphuric acid. Heat the mixture to 80°C in a water-bath, stirring constantly to prevent two layers forming. After about 5 min the mixture becomes homogeneous, and the reaction is completed by heating for a further 5 min. Remove the test-tube from the bath and cautiously add 10 ml of water, stirring vigorously. Cool the mixture to 10°C in an ice-bath and observe the crystalline product. If no crystals appear, scratch the inside of the tube with a glass rod.

(This will bring about the formation of crystals from a super-saturated solution.) Filter the product at a pump, and wash it with an ice-cold mixture of 3 ml concentrated hydrochloric acid (1) and 2 ml of water. Dry the product in a desiccator.

(1). The hydrochloric acid represses the solution of the *p*-xylene sulphonic acid. With water, a reaction occurs:

$$C_8H_9 . SO_3H + H_2O \rightleftharpoons C_8H_9 . SO_3^- + H_3O^+$$

Hydrochloric acid affords a high concentration of the H_3O^+ ion, and the reaction is repressed by the common ion.

Experiment 70. The preparation of ethyl iodide

$$3C_2H_5OH + PI_3 \rightarrow 3C_2H_5I + H_3PO_3$$

The phosphorus tri-iodide is made *in situ* by the reaction of red phosphorus and iodine.

Place $\frac{1}{2}$ g of red phosphorus in a pear-shaped flask and add 5 ml of industrial alcohol. Set a water condenser on the flask in the reflux position. Powder 5 g of iodine and add this to the flask in small

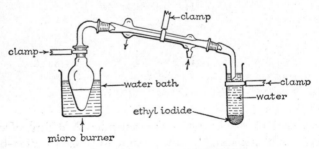

Fig. 39.—The preparation of ethyl iodide

portions, replacing the condenser after each addition so that there is no escape of volatile reactants or products. When all the iodine has been added, set the flask in a water-bath and allow the contents to reflux for $\frac{1}{2}$ hr (fig. 37 without the guard tube). Now connect the flask for normal distillation (fig. 39) collecting the product under water so that evaporation is avoided. Continue the distillation until no more drops of ethyl iodide come over. Transfer the contents of the test-tube to a separating funnel, collect the lower layer, and discard the upper. Impurities include iodine, and phosphoric acid. Wash the product with water, sodium carbonate solution, and finally water, in each case retaining the lower layer. Transfer the product into a test-tube, add anhydrous calcium chloride, cork the tube, and allow the product to dry for 20 min. Decant the dry ethyl iodide into a pear-shaped flask and determine its boiling point, using the method described in Experiment 2 (fig. 4). Weigh the product, and compare the yield with that calculated from the equation.

Experiment 71. The preparation of ethyl bromide

$$C_2H_5OH + HBr \rightarrow C_2H_5Br + H_2O$$

The hydrobromic acid is prepared *in situ* by the reaction of potassium bromide and sulphuric acid:

$$KBr + H_2SO_4 \rightarrow KHSO_4 + HBr$$

Set up the apparatus shown in fig. 39, omitting the water-bath. Place 2 ml of industrial alcohol in the flask, and mix this with 2 ml of concentrated sulphuric acid. The addition must be slow, and the flask must be shaken gently during the addition. Add $2\frac{1}{2}$ g of potassium bromide and connect the condenser immediately. Heat the flask using a small flame, avoiding excessive frothing by removing the source of heat. The ethyl bromide is collected under water (which prevents evaporation). Purify the product by the method described for ethyl iodide (Experiment 70).

Note.—Ethyl bromide boils at 38°C, and loss by evaporation during the purification is considerable. When the liquid is in contact with anhydrous calcium chloride, the tube should be stoppered with a cork wrapped in aluminium foil. This prevents diffusion of the vapour.

Experiment 72. The preparation of chloroform, $CHCl_3$

When bleaching powder reacts with acetone, a substitution reaction occurs:

$$CH_3.CO.CH_3 + 3Cl_2 \rightarrow CCl_3.CO.CH_3 + 3HCl$$

This reaction is followed by a hydrolysis of the product to form chloroform and calcium acetate.

$$2CCl_3.CO.CH_3 + Ca(OH)_2 \rightarrow 2CHCl_3 + (CH_3.COO)_2Ca$$

Method

Set up the apparatus for steam distillation (fig. 11). A 2-litre flask is useful in the preparation because considerable frothing occurs. Place 100 g of fresh bleaching powder in a large mortar and add 250 ml of water in small quantities. After each addition, grind the mixture well, decanting the 'cream' into the flask. Arrange the flask so that it may be connected to the steam generator and the condenser. Heat the generator until the water boils. Pour 30 ml of acetone into the flask and then immediately replace the stopper and connect the flask with the generator and the condenser. Blow steam through the mixture and collect water and chloroform in the receiver. When no more chloroform distils over, purify the product by washing it with water (removes acetone), dilute sodium hydroxide (chlorine), and finally water. Purification should be carried out using a separating funnel, and the lower layer retained in each case. Transfer the chloroform to a boiling-tube, add fused calcium chloride and stopper the tube. Allow the product to dry for 20 min, then decant the liquid into a small pear-shaped flask. Distil the product using the apparatus shown in fig. 4, collecting the fraction which boils at 60–63°C. Measure the yield of chloroform.

Reactions of chloroform

1. The carbylamine reaction. See Experiment 27.
2. Fehling's test. Boil a mixture of Fehling's solution and chloroform for several minutes. Observe that reduction occurs.

Experiment 73. The preparation of iodoform, CHI_3

The formula of iodoform suggests that it may be prepared in a manner similar to that used for the preparation of chloroform (Experiment 72). This proves to be the case. Compounds having as part of their structure the linkages

$$CH_3-CH- \quad \text{or} \quad CH_3-C-$$
$$\underset{OH}{|} \qquad\qquad \underset{O}{\|}$$

will yield iodoform when they react with iodine and then alkali. These linkages may be detected by conducting the Iodoform Test.

Method

(*a*) Add 6 g of potassium iodide to 100 ml of water in a flask. Add 2 ml of acetone and swirl the flask so that mixing is complete. Dilute 50 ml of commercial sodium hypochlorite (10–14%) with 50 ml of water, and slowly add the diluted solution to the flask. During the addition the flask should be swirled so that mixing is complete. Observe the formation of yellow crystals of iodoform; filter them at a pump, and wash them with water.

(*b*) Add 4 ml of industrial alcohol to 1 g of iodine in a test-tube. Add to the iodine solution 4 ml of 10% sodium hydroxide solution. Shake the tube and observe the formation of iodoform.

(*c*) Use method (*b*), but substitute methyl alcohol for the industrial alcohol (ethyl alcohol).

(*d*) Use method (*b*), but substitute isopropyl alcohol.

(*e*) Recrystallize a sample of iodoform from industrial alcohol (see Experiment 4); dry the product in an oven set at 50°C. Measure the melting point of the iodoform (119°C).

Experiment 74. The preparation of tribromoaniline

$$C_6H_5.NH_2 + 3Br_2 \rightarrow C_6H_2.NH_2.Br_3 + 3HBr$$

Add sufficient dilute hydrochloric acid to 1 ml of aniline to form a clear solution of aniline hydrochloride. Add bromine water and observe the immediate precipitation of tribromoaniline. Filter the product, wash it with water, dry it, and determine the melting point.

Experiment 75. The preparation of tribromophenol

$$C_6H_5.OH + 3Br_2 \rightarrow C_6H_2(OH).Br_3 + 3HBr$$

Dissolve a little phenol in water. Add bromine water and observe the precipitation of tribromophenol.

Experiment 76. The preparation of trinitrophenol (picric acid)

$$C_6H_5OH + 3HNO_3 \rightarrow C_6H_2(OH)(NO_2)_3 + 3H_2O$$

CAUTION: *Work in a fume cupboard. Oxides of nitrogen are evolved.*

Dissolve 2 g of phenol in 2 ml concentrated sulphuric acid contained in a test-tube, warming gently to bring about the solution. Cool the tube and add 2 ml of water. Now pour the solution into a boiling-tube containing 5 ml of concentrated nitric acid. Heat the tube in a water-bath for 10 min; oxides of nitrogen are evolved. Now pour the mixture into a beaker of cold water, adding the mixture slowly and stirring the water constantly. Filter the picric acid at a pump, wash it with water, dry it, and determine the melting point (122°C).

Experiment 77. The preparation of acetyl chloride

CAUTION: *This preparation must be done in a fume cupboard. Acetyl chloride vapour is highly toxic.*

Phosphorus trichloride replaces hydroxyl groups by chlorine atoms. When it reacts with acetic acid, acetyl chloride is produced.

$$3CH_3.COOH + PCl_3 \rightarrow 3CH_3.CO.Cl + H_3PO_3$$

Both the reactant PCl_3 and the product react with water, and for this reason every care must be taken to use a dry apparatus. The product must be collected in a dry atmosphere, and the guard tube provides this.

Method

Set up the apparatus shown in fig. 40. A three-necked flask is used, one neck taking a funnel, a second the distillation head, and the third is stoppered. The receiver is kept dry by attaching a soda lime tube at the outlet. The flask is set in a bath of cold water.

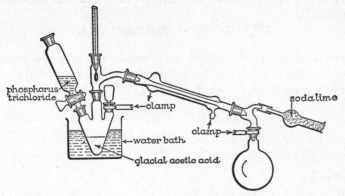

Fig. 40.—The preparation of acetyl chloride

Place 5 ml of glacial acetic acid in the flask and 4 ml of phosphorus trichloride in the funnel. Slowly add the phosphorus trichloride to the acid, and when addition is complete heat the water-bath to 40–45°C and maintain it at this temperature for 30 min. Heat the bath until the water boils, and collect the acetyl chloride. Boiling point 55°C.

Reactions of acetyl chloride

(1) On water. See Experiment 64.
(2) Acetylation of aniline. See Experiment 46.
(3) Acetylation of ethyl alcohol. See Experiment 45.
(4) Silver nitrate solution. Acidify a few millilitres of silver nitrate with dilute nitric acid. Add a few drops of acetyl chloride and note the formation of silver chloride.

Experiment 78. The preparation of sodium ethoxide

Sodium metal reacts with alcohols with the evolution of hydrogen gas. If ethyl alcohol is used, sodium ethoxide is formed.

$$2C_2H_5OH + 2Na \rightarrow 2C_2H_5O^-Na^+ + H_2$$

Any water in the alcohol will lead to the formation of sodium hydroxide.

$$2H_2O + 2Na \rightarrow 2Na^+OH^- + H_2$$

Metal derivatives of organic compounds are often important intermediates in syntheses. If we wish to prepare methyl ethyl ether, the following scheme might be adopted.

$$C_2H_5OH \overset{Na}{\rightarrow} C_2H_5ONa \quad \text{(sodium ethoxide)}$$

$$C_2H_5ONa + CH_3I \rightarrow \underset{\text{methyl ethyl ether}}{C_2H_5.O.CH_3} + NaI$$

Method

Place 10 ml of ethyl alcohol in an evaporating dish. Free from oil several small pieces of sodium by pressing them between filter paper. Add the sodium to the alcohol. When the reaction stops, set the evaporating dish on a water-bath and drive off excess alcohol. Observe the white solid which remains.

Degradation Reactions

16

When reaction results in a product whose molecules contain fewer carbon atoms than are contained in the reactant, then the process is termed a *degradation*. This type of reaction is important in the chemical industry. The dry distillation of coal or wood with the production of simple organic compounds, and the more recent process of 'cracking' hydrocarbon oils are all degradation processes.

Experiment 79. The preparation of methane (CH_4) *from sodium acetate* ($CH_3COO^-Na^+$)

When a mixture of fused sodium acetate and soda lime is strongly heated, then methane is evolved and may be collected by the displacement of water. Soda lime is a mixture of lime and sodium hydroxide; it is manufactured by slaking lime with sodium hydroxide solution and roasting the product.

$$CH_3COONa + NaOH \rightarrow CH_4 + Na_2CO_3$$
$$CH_3COO^- + OH^- \rightarrow CH_4 + CO_3^{--}$$

Method

Powder 10 g of fused sodium acetate and mix it with 20 g of soda lime. Transfer the mixture to a hard-glass boiling-tube, connect a delivery tube as shown in fig. 41, heat the mixture strongly, and collect the methane as shown. Experiment 25 describes tests which may be conducted on the product. The residue in the boiling-tube may be tested for the carbonate ion by adding dilute hydrochloric acid. The evolution of carbon dioxide is immediate, and a lime-water test may be carried out.

Predict the products formed when the following mixtures are heated:

(i) Benzoic acid (C_6H_5COOH) and soda lime.
(ii) Salicylic acid ($HO.C_6H_4.COOH$) and soda lime.

Prepare these mixtures and heat them; identify the products by their odours.

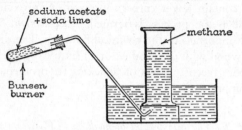

Fig. 41.—The preparation of methane

Experiment 80. The preparation of acetone ($CH_3.CO.CH_3$) *from calcium acetate* ($CH_3.COO)_2Ca$

When calcium acetate is strongly heated acetone is produced. The yield is small and is very impure.

$$(CH_3.COO)_2Ca \rightarrow CH_3.CO.CH_3 + CaCO_3$$
$$2CH_3COO^- \rightarrow CH_3.CO.CH_3 + CO_3^{--}$$

Set up the apparatus shown in fig. 42. Place calcium acetate in the boiling-tube and connect to a Liebig condenser. Pass water through the condenser and strongly heat the tube. Collect the impure acetone in a small measuring cylinder.

Perform the iodoform test on the product (Experiment 73).

Experiment 81. The preparation of methylamine (CH_3NH_2) *from acetamide* ($CH_3.CO.NH_2$). *Hofmann's descent of series*

When an amide ($R.CO.NH_2$) is treated with bromine and potassium hydroxide, a degradation reaction occurs and an amine

$(R.NH_2)$ is formed. This reaction is an important method of preparing amines; it is also a common method for the descent of a homologous series. As an example of this, the conversion of ethyl to methyl alcohol will be considered.

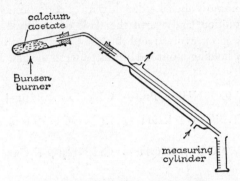

Fig. 42.—The preparation of acetone

$$C_2H_5OH \xrightarrow[\substack{H_2SO_4 \\ [\text{Exp. 31}]}]{K_2Cr_2O_7} CH_3.COOH$$

ethyl alcohol   acetic acid

$$CH_3.COOH + NH_4OH \longrightarrow CH_3.COO.NH_4 + H_2O$$

ammonium acetate

$$CH_3.COO.NH_4 \xrightarrow[\substack{CH_3.COOH \\ [\text{Exp. 58}]}]{\text{heat}} CH_3.CO.NH_2 + H_2O$$

acetamide

$$CH_3.CO.NH_2 \xrightarrow[\text{heat}]{Br/KOH} CH_3.NH_2$$

methylamine

$$CH_3.NH_2 \xrightarrow[HCl]{NaNO_2} CH_3OH$$

methyl alcohol

Side reactions in the final stage produce methyl nitrite and dimethyl ether, so that the yield of alcohol is low.

Method

CAUTION. Wear rubber gloves when handling bromine.

Place 2 g of acetamide and 1·5 ml of bromine in a small flask, cool the mixture, and add dilute potassium hydroxide solution until the colour of bromine is discharged. Add 5 ml of concentrated potassium hydroxide solution, and warm the flask on a tripod and gauze. Methylamine gas is evolved and this may be detected by its 'fishy' smell, also by holding moist red litmus paper in the gas. The paper is turned blue.

$$CH_3.CO.NH_2 + Br_2 \rightarrow CH_3.CO.NHBr + HBr$$

$$CH_3.CO.NHBr + KOH \rightarrow \underset{\text{methyl isocyanate}}{CH_3.NCO} + KBr + H_2O$$

$$CH_3.NCO + 2KOH \rightarrow CH_3NH_2 + K_2CO_3$$

Molecular Weight Determinations

17

The quantitative analysis of a compound gives knowledge of the empirical formula of the substance, i.e. it gives us the simplest number ratio of atoms present in a molecule. If the empirical formula is $C_xH_yO_z$, the true formula must be some multiple of this, $C_{nx}H_{ny}O_{nz}$, where n might be 1, 2, 3, ...; n is determined by molecular weight measurement. For this purpose, it is unnecessary to measure the molecular weight to a high degree of accuracy, and some of the methods provide a rough answer only.

Methods may be divided into two groups:

A. *Physical methods*
 1. Victor Meyer's method. Vapour density determination.
 2. Dumas' method. Vapour density determination.
 3. Cryoscopic method. Depression of freezing point.
 4. Ebullioscopic method. Elevation of boiling point.

B. *Chemical methods*
 1. Titration methods.
 2. Gravimetric methods.

The limitations of each method will be discussed in the descriptions which follow. Physical methods are covered in texts on physical chemistry and will not be considered further.

Experiment 82. The molecular weight of an acid (by titration)

Molecular weight of acid = equivalent weight × basicity

The equivalent weight may be determined by titrating the acid against standard alkali; the basicity is determined by a study of the salts which the acid is able to form. If experiment shows that sodium hydroxide combines with the acid to form one salt only, then this is good evidence that the acid is monobasic. If two sodium salts exist, then the acid is probably dibasic, etc. Because equivalent weights may be determined with a high degree of accuracy, the molecular weights obtained by this method are also very accurate, provided the correct basicity is substituted.

Method (*Use propionic acid*)

Clean and dry a weighing bottle, then weigh it accurately. Place about 1 ml of freshly distilled propionic acid in the bottle and weigh it again. Transfer the acid to a 250-ml graduated flask, rinse the bottle, and transfer the wash water into the flask. Make up to the mark with distilled water and mix the solution thoroughly. Pipette three 25-ml portions of the dilute solution into separate conical flasks. Titrate these with decinormal sodium hydroxide solution, using phenolphthalein as the indicator.

Results

Weight of the acid w g

25·0 ml of the dilute solution required y ml of xN NaOH.

Normality of the acid solution is $\dfrac{y}{25} \times x$

Weight of acid in one litre of solution is $4w$ g

Normality of the acid is $\dfrac{4w}{E}$ (E is the equivalent weight of the acid)

$$\therefore \frac{4w}{E} = \frac{y}{25} \times x$$

$$E = \frac{100 \times w}{y \times x}$$

Propionic acid is monobasic, so that the molecular weight is numerically equal to the equivalent weight.

Experiment 83. The molecular weight of a base (aniline)

If the hydrochloride of a weak base is titrated with a standard alkali, the following reaction occurs:

$$RNH_3^+ + OH^- \rightarrow R.NH_2 + H_2O$$
free base

Completion of the reaction may be marked by using an indicator which is unaffected by the free base. Titration allows the calculation of the equivalent weight of the hydrochloride salt, and if the base is known to be monoacid, then its molecular weight is less than that of the salt by the equivalent of hydrochloric acid (36·5).

Method

Weigh accurately 1·50–2·00 g of aniline hydrochloride. Transfer the solid to a 100-ml graduated flask and make up to the mark with distilled water. Shake the solution to ensure a thorough mixing. Pipette two 25-ml portions into separate conical flasks, add a few drops of phenolphthalein, and titrate with decinormal sodium hydroxide solution.

Results

Weight of the aniline hydrochloride	x g
Average titration value (0·1N . NaOH)	v ml
Normality of the hydrochloride solution	$v/250$
Weight of the salt/litre	$10x$ g
Normality of the solution (E = equivalent weight of salt)	$\dfrac{10x}{E}$

$$\therefore \frac{10x}{E} = \frac{v}{250}$$

$$E = \frac{2500x}{v}$$

The molecular weight of aniline is $\left(\dfrac{2500x}{v} - 36\cdot5\right)$

Experiment 84. The molecular weight of acids by analysis of their silver salts

The advantages of the method are:

(*a*) Silver salts may be isolated easily because they are only sparingly soluble in water.

(*b*) They rarely contain water of crystallization, so that their composition will not vary according to the degree of hydration.

(*c*) On heating they yield pure silver, and this does not oxidize.

The limitations of the method include:

(*a*) The silver salts of some acids decompose violently on heating, and solids might be lost.

(*b*) If the acid contains halogen atoms, then silver halides remain as the residue after heating.

(*c*) The silver salts of carboxylic acids are soluble in acid solutions, so that care must be taken to neutralize solutions before attempting the precipitation of the silver salts. Neutralization must be effected by using ammonia solution, because sodium hydroxide precipitates silver oxide.

Method

Dissolve 1 ml of glacial acetic acid in 30 ml of distilled water. Add dilute ammonia to the solution, stirring continuously, until the resulting solution just smells of ammonia. Boil the solution until no more ammonia is evolved and then allow the solution to cool. Precipitate silver acetate by adding 10% silver nitrate solution, and continue the addition until no more solid is precipitated. Filter the silver acetate at a pump using a small funnel. Wash the precipitate with distilled water, transfer it to a small dish, and set this in a desiccator. Leave the solid drying for a week, storing the desiccator in a cupboard to exclude light.

Heat a clean crucible and lid, supporting them on a pipe-clay triangle, and then allow them to cool in a desiccator. Weigh the crucible and lid. Introduce the silver acetate, replace the lid, and weigh the crucible and solid. Place the crucible on the triangle, and heat it to decompose the silver acetate. Heating should be gentle at first, and the crucible must be fanned with a Bunsen flame. After ten minutes the flame should be increased until the crucible is glowing red. Continue heating for five minutes with the Bunsen set underneath the triangle. Cool the crucible in a desiccator and weigh it again. Reheat, cool, and weigh it again. Continue to constant weight.

Calculation

Weight of the silver acetate w_1 g

Weight of the silver $\quad\quad\quad w_2$ g

$$\frac{\text{equivalent of silver}}{\text{equivalent of silver acetate}} = \frac{\text{weight of silver}}{\text{weight of silver acetate}}$$

$$\frac{107 \cdot 9}{107 \cdot 9 + \text{equivalent of acetate ion}} = \frac{w_2}{w_1}$$

$$\text{Equivalent of the acetate ion} = 107 \cdot 9 \frac{w_1}{w_2} - 107 \cdot 9$$

$$\text{Equivalent of acetic acid} = 107 \cdot 9 \frac{w_1}{w_2} - 107 \cdot 9 + 1$$

Acetic acid is monobasic, so that its equivalent weight is numerically equal to its molecular weight.

The Identification of Organic Compounds

18

The identification of organic compounds is something of an art. Simple inorganic chemicals, or even mixtures of them, may be identified by a rigid application of some scheme of analysis, but this is not nearly so true of organic compounds. It is possible to construct inorganic mixtures which will defy a scheme of analysis, and which will make the analyst think for himself, but the identification of an organic substance will usually demand personal initiative. The analyst must exercise his knowledge all the time.

In this work, the full recording of tests and observations is of vital importance. If a single test gives conclusive evidence of the nature of a substance, then there is no problem in remembering that it was positive, neither does the statement of the conclusion require thought. These clear and obvious conclusions are uncommon when dealing with organic chemicals. An accumulation of observations points the way. Individual observations may well be meaningless at the time. So it is that a full record of tests and observations must be taken during the analysis.

It is faster, safer, and more economical to use small quantities of a substance for its analysis. Remember that a test-tube ought not to be more than one-third full.

The analysis of an organic mixture is complicated by the fact that it must be resolved, and the purity of the components judged, before any other work is carried out. The techniques for separation and for judging purity are given in chapters 2, 3, and 4, but the suggested scheme which follows relates to single substances only.

SCHEME OF ANALYSIS

A. Preliminary tests

Preliminary tests serve to indicate which active groups are present.

B. Confirmatory tests

Confirmatory tests serve to confirm an initial judgement and will often point to an individual compound containing the active group or groups.

C. Reference to lists of physical constants

The boiling point or melting point of the substance is compared with those of known compounds, and final identification is made. It sometimes happens that several possible compounds have the same characteristics, and the method of mixed melting points proves useful (see p. 4).

D. The preparation of a derivative

Confidence in the conclusion is enhanced if the substance is found to provide a predicted derivative. If, for example, a substance has been identified as ethyl alcohol, then it ought to be possible to prepare ethyl acetate from it.

Preliminary tests

1. Note the appearance and the odour of the substance

Nothing can replace a direct experience of organic chemicals. Time spent in the chemical store, looking at and smelling the chemicals, will prove invaluable. Inspect the following so that you recognize them in future:

methyl alcohol	acetaldehyde	acetamide
ethyl alcohol	formalin	ethyl acetate
chloroform	acetone	aniline
iodoform	diethyl ether	benzene
	formic acid	nitrobenzene
	acetic acid	benzaldehyde
		phenol

2. Determine the boiling point or the melting point

Experiments 1 and 2. Pay particular attention to signs of decomposition, or to sublimation, which might occur during the determinations.

3. Observe the action of water, cold, then hot. Add litmus

Many water-soluble substances contain hydroxyl or carbonyl groups. Note any signs of reaction with the water. The reddening of litmus does not necessarily mean that the substance is an acid; it may be that acids result from the hydrolysis of the substance, e.g. acid chlorides, acid anhydrides, or esters. Similarly, litmus will be turned blue not only by bases, but by salts of weak acids, e.g. sodium acetate.

4. Observe the action of cold dilute hydrochloric acid

If the substance is water-soluble, this does not provide much information. Solution of an insoluble substance indicates that it is a base, probably an amine. The acidification of an aqueous solution, resulting in the formation of a precipitate, might indicate that the substance is the soluble salt of an insoluble acid.

5. Observe the action of cold dilute sodium hydroxide solution

If the substance is water-soluble, add the alkali to an aqueous solution. The liberation of an oil indicates that the substance is the salt of a base, e.g. aniline sulphate, the oil being the free base. The rapid solution of a water-insoluble compound indicates that it is an acid (carboxylic or phenolic).

6. To distinguish phenolic from carboxylic acids

If Test 5 indicates that the substance is a carboxylic acid or a phenol, add a little sodium bicarbonate solution to the substance. Carboxylic acids cause the evolution of carbon dioxide, phenols do not. (A compound might contain both groups, e.g. salicylic acid $HO . C_6H_4 . COOH$.)

7. Detect the presence of halogens, nitrogen, sulphur

See Experiment 21.

8. *Observe the action of hot sodium hydroxide solution*

Some aliphatic aldehydes form a yellow-red resin (Experiment 40). Esters will be saponified and the fragrant odour disappears (Experiment 61) though this is a slow process.

If the substance is nitrogenous, the test is most instructive.

(a) The rapid evolution of ammonia indicates an *ammonium salt*.
(b) The slow evolution of ammonia indicates an amide linkage —CO—NH$_2$, or possibly a nitrile —CN.

9. *Place the substance on a crucible lid and heat it strongly*

A residue indicates that the substance is a metal salt (Experiment 18). The nature of the anion and cation may be determined using normal qualitative techniques. If the substance burns, note the appearance of the flame. If this is clean, then a low-molecular-weight aliphatic compound is indicated. A sooty flame is characteristic of aromatic compounds.

10. *Observe the action of bromine water*

Phenols and aromatic amines decolorize bromine water and produce white precipitates. Unsaturated compounds, e.g. those containing the linkage —C=C—, also bring about decolorization. Great care must be taken in interpreting the results here; remember that bromine can oxidize, substitute, or add.

11. *Carry out the Fehling's test* (Experiment 36)

If this is positive, then the substance is a strong reducing agent, but this may be due to a number of active groups.

Most aliphatic aldehydes give the test, together with a few ketones, formates, several alcohols and phenols, and chloroform.

CONSULT THE TABLE ON PP. 142–3 AND DECIDE UPON THE TYPE OF SUBSTANCE, THEN DO THE RELATED CONFIRMATORY TESTS, RECONSIDERING YOUR JUDGEMENT. Table 2.

TABLE 1

Elements present 7	Soluble in water 1	Insoluble H$_2$O soluble dilute HCl 2	Insoluble H$_2$O soluble cold NaOH 3
C, H, possibly O	lower alcohols lower carboxylic acids lower aldehydes lower ketones phenols (sparingly) acid anhydrides (with decomposition)		carboxylic acids phenols
C, H, N, possibly O	lower aliphatic amines amides nitriles NH$_4^+$ salts	higher aliphatic amines aromatic amines	nitrophenols
C, H, halogen, possibly O	substituted carboxylic acids acyl halides (decomposed)		halogen substituted phenols
C, H, S, possibly O	sulphonic acids aldehyde and ketone bisulphites		
C, H, N, halogen, possibly O	hydracids of amines	halogenated aromatic amines	
C, H, N, S, possibly O	amine sulphates		amino sulphonic acids

TABLE 1.—*Continued*

Evolution of NH_3 with NaOH 8	Fehling's positive 11	Bromine water positive 10	Insoluble 1, 2, 3
	most aldehydes formates	phenols unsaturated compounds	hydrocarbons ethers esters higher alcohols higher aldehydes higher ketones
cold, NH_4^+ salts hot, amides hot, nitriles		aromatic amines	nitro compounds
			substituted hydrocarbons eg. alkyl halide
sulphonamides $—SO_2 . NH_2$			

TABLE 2.—GROUP CONFIRMATORY TESTS

Group	Tests
Alcohol	1. Add sodium and observe the continuous evolution of H_2. [Experiment 78] 2. Add glacial acetic acid and a drop of concentrated H_2SO_4. Warm and observe the smell of an ester. [Experiment 44] 3. Add $K_2Cr_2O_7$ solution + dilute H_2SO_4. Warm. [Experiment 31] Primary alcohols oxidized —CH_2—OH → —CHO (Solution → green) Secondary alcohols oxidized $\geq$CH—OH→ $\geq$C=O (Solution → green) Tertiary alcohols—no action
Carboxylic acids	1. Add $NaHCO_3$ solution. Note the evolution of CO_2. 2. Add a little methyl alcohol + drop of concentrated H_2SO_4. Warm and observe the smell of an ester. [Experiment 44]
Phenols	1. Add neutral ferric chloride solution to an aqueous solution of the phenol. Blue, purple, or green colour is obtained. [Experiment 31 for the preparation of $FeCl_3$ reagent] 2. Dissolve the phenol in sodium hydroxide solution, add a solution of phenyldiazonium chloride and observe the formation of a dye. [See Experiment 41 for the preparation of the diazonium compound.]

TABLE 2.—*Continued*

Group	Tests
Amines	1. Perform the *carbylamine reaction*. Take a drop of the amine, add a drop of chloroform and a little alcoholic KOH. Warm the mixture. The evolution of a carbylamine (unpleasant and persistent odour) indicates *primary amine* R—NH$_2$. [Carbylamines contain the linkage R—NC.] 2. If Test 1 is negative, dissolve the amine in dilute HCl, and add a cold solution of sodium nitrite. The formation of a light yellow oil indicates that the amine is *secondary* $\overset{R}{\underset{R}{>}}$NH (possibly a tertiary aromatic amine.) $$\left[\overset{R}{\underset{R}{>}}NH + HO.NO \rightarrow \overset{R}{\underset{R}{>}}N.NO + H_2O \right]$$ nitroso oil
Aldehydes and Ketones	1. Shake with a concentrated solution of NaHSO$_3$. Note the formation of a crystalline bisulphite derivative. [See Experiment 49] 2. Shake with phenylhydrazine solution. The slow formation of a hydrazone derivative indicates a carbonyl linkage. [See Experiment 37] 2:4 *dinitro phenylhydrazine* (NO$_2$)$_2$C$_6$H$_3$.NH.NH$_2$ is a better reagent than unsubstituted phenylhydrazine, formation of crystalline hydrazones being more rapid. Dissolve a little dinitro phenylhydrazine in a few drops of concentrated H$_2$SO$_4$, and dilute the solution with a little methyl alcohol. Add the suspected aldehyde in methyl alcohol solution, shake the mixture and observe hydrazone formation.

TABLE 2.—*Continued*

Group	Tests
Nitro	1. Often yellow in colour. 2. They may be reduced to primary amines and these are easily acetylated. Take equal volumes of glacial acetic acid and acetic anhydride. Add the suspected nitro compound and an excess of zinc dust. Reflux the mixture for ten minutes. Filter the hot solution, add water to the filtrate, and observe the precipitation of an acetylated amine. [See Experiment 46]
Acyl halides R . CO . Cl	1. Add a little to water, observe the evolution of HCl. Acidify the resulting solution with HNO_3, add $AgNO_3$ solution. Observe the precipitation of silver halide. 2. Add a few drops to ethyl alcohol, observe the smell of an ester. [Experiment 45]
Salts of amines	Dissolve the substance in water, add sodium hydroxide solution, and observe the liberation of the base. The lowest amines are water-soluble, but when the solution is boiled, the 'fishy' smell of an amine may be detected.
Esters	1. Strong fruity smell. 2. Reflux with aqueous sodium hydroxide. The ester smell disappears. 3. Mix 0·88 ammonia and the suspected ester in a boiling-tube, stopper the tube, and set it in a warm place. Shake the mixture occasionally and allow the reaction to continue until the mixture is homogeneous. [During the reaction an amide is formed: $R . CO . OR^1 + NH_3 \rightarrow R . CO . NH_2 + R^1 . OH$ Hydrocarbons and ethers will not form a homogeneous mixture with concentrated ammonia.]

PHYSICAL EVIDENCE OF THE IDENTITY OF THE COMPOUND

The table lists the melting and/or boiling points of most organic chemicals encountered in junior laboratories. Having determined which type of compound you are dealing with, consult the relevant chart, and decide upon the individual member.

TABLE 3.—ALCOHOLS

Name	Formula	Boiling point, °C	Comments
methyl	$CH_3 . OH$	65	Iodoform test negative [Exp. 73]
ethyl	$C_2H_5 . OH$	78	Iodoform test positive [Exp. 73]
iso-propyl	$(CH_3)_2CH . OH$	82	Iodoform test positive Heat with $K_2Cr_2O_7/H_2SO_4$ Smell of acetone
n-propyl	$CH_3(CH_2)_2 . OH$	97	
iso-butyl	$(CH_3)_2CH . CH_2 . OH$	108	
n-butyl	$CH_3(CH_2)_3 . OH$	118	
cyclohexanol	$C_6H_{11} . OH$	161	
ethylene glycol	$C_2H_4(OH)_2$	197	
benzyl alcohol	$C_6H_5 . CH_2 . OH$	205	
glycerol	$CH_2 . OH$ $\|$ $CH . OH$ $\|$ $CH_2 . OH$	290 (with dec.)	

TABLE 4.—HALOGEN-SUBSTITUTED HYDROCARBONS

Name	Formula	Boiling point, °C		
		chloride	bromide	iodide
methyl	CH_3X	—	—	42
ethyl	C_2H_5X	—	38	73
iso-propyl	$(CH_3)_2CH.X$	35	59	89
n-propyl	$CH_3.(CH_2)_2X$	46	71	102
ethylene	$C_2H_4X_2$	83	131	
benzyl	$C_6H_5.CH_2.X$	179	198	
chloroform	$CHCl_3$	61	Carbylamine test positive. See test for primary amines.	
iodoform	CHI_3	M.P. 119	Yellow crystals	
chlorobenzene	C_6H_5Cl	132		
bromobenzene	C_6H_5Br	156		

Table 5.—BASES

Name	Formula	M.P., °C	B.P., °C	Comments
aniline	$C_6H_5NH_2$		183	Prepare acetyl deriva-
o-toluidine	$CH_3.C_6H_4.NH_2$		200	tives [Exp. 46] M.P. 110°C
m-toluidine	$CH_3.C_6H_4.NH_2$		203	M.P. 65°C
p-toluidine	$CH_3.C_6H_4.NH_2$	44	200	
methylaniline	$C_6H_5.NH.CH_3$		194	
dimethylaniline	$C_6H_5.N.(CH_3)_2$		193	No acetyl derivative may be prepared
diphenylamine	$(C_6H_5)_2N.H$	54	302	

Acid	Formula	M.P., °C	B.P., °C	B.P., °C anhydride	B.P., °C chloride	M.P., °C amide	B.P., °C nitrile
formic	H . COOH		101				
acetic	CH₃ . COOH		118	140	52	82	82
propionic	C₂H₅ . COOH		140	168	80	79	97
oxalic	(COOH)₂	cryst. 100 anhy. 187	(Warm concentrated H₂SO₄. CO/CO₂ evolution.)				No colour change.
benzoic	C₆H₅ . COOH	122			197	128	189
succinic	(CH₂)₂(COOH)₂	185		m.p. 119			
phthalic (decomp.)	C₆H₄(COOH)₂	208		m.p. 132			
maleic (unsat.)	CH . COOH ‖ CH . COOH	135		m.p. 56			
cinnamic (unsat.)	C₆H₅ . CH=CH . COOH	133					
citric (hydrate)	C(OH) . COOH — CH₂ . COOH	100	(Warm with concentrated H₂SO₄. Turns yellow. Evolution CO/CO₂.)				
salicylic	HO . C₆H₄ . COOH	159	(Neutral ferric chloride indicates phenolic compound.)				
d-tartaric	CH(OH) . COOH — CH(OH) . COOH	168	(Warm with concentrated H₂SO₄. Blackens with effervescence.)				
trichloracetic	CCl₃ . COOH	58					
monochloracetic	CH₂Cl . COOH	63					
anthranilic	NH₂ . C₆H₄ . COOH	146					
glycine (decomp.)	NH₂ . CH₂ . COOH	262					

149

TABLE 7.—ALDEHYDES AND KETONES

Name	Formula	M.P., °C	B.P., °C	Comments	
acetaldehyde	CH_3CHO		21	Fehling's positive	Iodoform positive
benzaldehyde	$C_6H_5.CHO$		179	Fehling's negative	Iodoform negative
acetone	$(CH_3)_2CO$		56	Fehling's negative	Iodoform positive
methyl-ethyl ketone	$CH_3.CO.C_2H_5$		79		
cyclohexanone	$(CH_2)_5CO$		155		
acetophenone	$C_6H_5.CO.CH_3$	20	202		
benzophenone	$(C_6H_5)_2CO$	49	306		

TABLE 8.—PHENOLS

Name	Formula	M.P., °C	B.P., °C	Colour given by* phthalein test
m-cresol	$CH_3.C_6H_4OH$		202	bluish purple
o-cresol	$CH_3.C_6H_4OH$	30	191	red
p-cresol	$CH_3.C_6H_4OH$	34	202	
phenol	C_6H_5OH	43	182	red
α-naphthol	$C_{10}H_7OH$	94		very faint green
catechol	$C_6H_4(OH)_2^{(1:2)}$	104	240	blue
resorcinol	$C_6H_4(OH)_2^{(1:3)}$	110		green fluorescence
β-naphthol	$C_{10}H_7.OH$	123		green
pyrogallol	$C_6H_3(OH)_3^{(1:2:3)}$	133		
o-chlorophenol	$C_6H_4.(OH).Cl$		175	
p-chlorophenol	$C_6H_4(OH).Cl$	43	217	
o-nitrophenol	$NO_2.C_6H_4.OH$	44		
p-nitrophenol	$NO_2.C_6H_4OH$	114		
picric acid	$(NO_2)_3.C_6H_2OH$	122		

*The phthalein test

Place a little of the phenol in a dry test-tube, add a little phthalic anhydride, and moisten the mixture with concentrated H_2SO_4. Heat the mixture gently for about one minute, allow it to cool, and add bench sodium hydroxide in excess. Observe the colour produced. (See Experiment 42.)

TABLE 9.—ETHERS

Name	Formula	B.P., °C
diethyl	$(C_2H_5)_2O$	34
anisole	$C_6H_5 . O . CH_3$	153

TABLE 10.—ESTERS

Acid	Methyl B.P., °C	Ethyl B.P., °C
formic	31	54
acetic	57	77
propionic	80	98
oxalic	163 (m.p. 54)	183
benzoic	199	213
salicylic	223	231

The nature of the ester may be further confirmed by refluxing it with dilute sodium hydroxide for 30 min, following this by a normal distillation to collect the alcohol obtained.

Distillate

Perform the iodoform reaction (Experiment 73). A positive result indicates ethyl alcohol; negative, methyl alcohol.

Residual solution (after cooling)

Acidify with dilute H_2SO_4. A white precipitate indicates an *aromatic acid*. If there is no precipitate then the acid is water-soluble. Distil the acid solution and test the distillate for formic and acetic acid.

(a) Immediate decolorization of alkaline $KMnO_4$ (Experiment 51 (ii)) indicates FORMIC ACID.

(b) Negative (a), but a positive neutral ferric chloride test, indicates ACETIC ACID (Experiment 31).

If no acid is detected in the distillate, then the acid is not volatile. Examine the residual solution in the distillation flask.

(c) Warm the solution, add $KMnO_4$ solution. Decolorization indicates OXALIC ACID.

TABLE 11.—HYDROCARBONS

Name	Formula	B.P., °C
benzene	C_6H_6	80
cyclohexane	C_6H_{12}	81
toluene	$C_6H_5 . CH_3$	110
m-xylene	$C_6H_4 . (CH_3)_2$	139
naphthalene	$C_{10}H_8$	m.p. 80
anthracene	$C_{14}H_{10}$	m.p. 217

TABLE 12.—SPECIMEN REPORT

Test	Observation	Conclusion
1. Appearance Smell	colourless liquid fruity	Ester?
2. Boiling point	76°C	
3. Water	insoluble, litmus reddened	
4. Dilute HCl	insoluble	
5. Cold dilute NaOH	insoluble	What of 3? Impurity?
7. For N, S, halogens	negative	
8. Hot NaOH solution	the smell faded slowly	Ester? or loss by evaporation?
9. Heated on lid	no residue, no smoke	It is not a salt and it is not aromatic
10. Bromine water	it was not decolorized	Saturated
11. Fehling's test	there was a slight reduction	It is worth testing for aldehyde

Confirmatory tests

The preliminary tests indicate that the substance is an ester. Alcohols of this boiling point would be water-soluble, and the same is true of aldehydes and ketones. The substance does not smell like a hydrocarbon. Confirm these comments.

TABLE 12.—*Continued*

Test	Observation	Conclusion
12. Addition of a piece of sodium	no action	not an alcohol
13. Addition of 2:4 dinitro phenylhydrazine	no action	not an aldehyde or ketone
14. Refluxed with dilute NaOH	the smell disappeared	not an ether or a hydrocarbon
15. The refluxed mixture was distilled and an iodoform reaction conducted on the distillate	positive	
16. The residual liquid was acidified with dilute H_2SO_4	no precipitate	the acid part of the ester is water-soluble
17. Distil the acid solution	distillate had a smell of acetic acid	
18. Neutral ferric chloride on the distillate	red coloration	acetic acid

The substance is ETHYL ACETATE. [*Text b.p.* 77°C]

INDEX